U.S. Guns of World War II

Record of Army Ordnance
Research and Development on Small Arms

Firefight on Okinawa

Marine Corps Historical Center

Paul J. Davies

Thomas Publications
Gettysburg, Pa.

US Army Military History Institute

Infantrymen of the 5th Infantry Division, 11th Infantry Regiment, carrying a boat to the Moselle River near Dordot, France on 8 September 1944. The soldier on the left is carrying a 1903 rifle, the GI next to him carries an M1 with a M7 grenade launcher — the rest M1 Garands. The contributing author's Uncle Sgt. John E. Green crossed the Moselle in this attack in such a boat. He was severely wounded at Metz in the attack on the German occupied Fort Driant and had to be evacuated by swimming back across the Moselle. Uncle Jack carried a BAR in Normandy. The only words on the war he ever said to the author were during a Christmas visit; viewing a scene in "The Big Red One" of extended BAR firing, Uncle Jack said, "No, one burst and roll."

Published by   THOMAS PUBLICATIONS
                        P.O. Box 3031
                        Gettysburg, Pa. 17325

Printed and bound in the United States of America

ISBN 1-57747-105-9

Layout, Cover, and new Photography by Paul J. Davies

Back Cover Painting: "A Flower for a B.A.R. Man" by Michelle A. Davies, 2003

Dedicated to all the GI's who served our Country

Family members in WWII included:

Uncle Addie — Adam W. Davies, Aviation Machinist's Mate.
Norman, Oklahoma & Johnston Island, Middle of Pacific.

George T. McMahon, Corporal, Co. A, 823rd Tank Destroyer
Battalion, 1st Army. Normandy, Battle of Mortain, Falaise,
Ardennes. Severely wounded in a M10 tank destroyer in
Belgium, 19 December 1944, in the Battle of the Bulge.
Received three Bronze Stars and the Purple Heart.

George W. Bittner, Pfc., Co. "E", 194th Glider Infantry Regt.,
17th Airborne Div., Battle of Bulge, Operation Varsity.

And the war workers; at home in Philadelphia included:

Adam R. Davies	- Frankford Arsenal
Harry J. Davies	- Naval Aircraft Factory
Marie R. Davies	- Frankford Arsenal
Dorothy Green	- Henry Disston & Sons, Inc.
Frank P. Green	- Plumb Tool
Margaret Green	- Quaker City Iron
Betty Jenkins	- Frankford Arsenal

Dad — Harry J. Davies, 3rd Class Petty Officer, Aviation Metalsmith aboard Carrier USS Bennington, CV-20, August 1945 on a SB2C Helldiver dive bomber. Near miss by landing fighter. To have been landing craft coxswain in Invasion of Japan.

Uncle Jack - S/Sgt. John L. Fox, Jr. (4th left bottom) & crew., 360th Bombardment Squadron, 8th Air Force - asst. engineer & gunner. Shot down over Hamburg, Germany 20 June 1944 on 19th mission. Capt John Parker (center top) crash landed their B-17 with 4 dead engines - all survived. Uncle Jack was a POW at Stalag Luft IV, enduring a winter march - Purple Heart. Sold his Luger for $200 to a sailor on LST trip home.

Uncle Frank W. Green, Sgt., 80th Division, Right, on Sherman Tank - "Belgium 1944", V-2 near miss in England, fought in Battle of Kassel, Liberation of concentration camp. Wound up with a sack of Lugers in Norway, courtesy the British 1st Airborne. Family tradition is he lost most in the crap games on troopship home - but kept a Luger, dagger & officer's hat.

"Austria, May 1st, 1945. Wm. Martz, my ex-ass't squad leader. I may look heavier there, but it isn't true. Merely a pistol under my jacket." John E. Green

Uncle Jack - John E. Green, right, S/Sgt. 5th Div., 11th Infantry Regiment, Co. E, 3rd Army. Bronze Star, Purple Heart. Fought in Normandy, Battle of Bulge and Crossing the Rhine. Wounded at Fort Driant and Battle of Bulge. Lost his captured P-38 in a card game on the way home. Back in U.S. on V-J Day training for the Invasion of Japan. He only talked of the war at age 70.

Joined U.S.M.C. on 17th Birthday 9 April 1942 Discharged 30 December 1945

Uncle Bill, William R. Miller, U.S.M.C., Joined Marines age 17. 3rd Service Battalion, 3rd Marine Division, Cook & Baker, Holds a M1903 rifle, Parris Island, South Carolina, May 1942. Spent 22 months on New Caledonia, Guadalcanal, and Guam. At war's end was ready to embark for the Invasion of Japan.

**And to President Harry Truman
who ordered the dropping of the
Atomic Bombs ending the war.**

3

USAMHI

"Beffe, Belgium. S/Sgt Urban Minicozzi (Jessup, Pa) Hqs. Co. and Pfc. Andy Masiero (Newburg, N.Y.) Co. A. both of 1st Bn. 290th Infantry Regiment, 75th Inf. Div., 7th Corps, Troop B, 4th Cav Reconn. Sq. stop to reload while sniping snipers from the roof of a building. 1/7/45" Both have M1 Garand rifles, with Private Masiero about to put an 8-round clip into his M1 Garand rifle.

USAMHI

191196

"American troops of the 93rd Div. (Colored), on patrol in Jap territory, ran into a superior Japanese force. The patrol occupied an apparently deserted Jap bivouac area — then was attacked. The photo shows one of the Colored soldiers firing from the prone position from just outside this Jap leanto. Legs in the foreground belong to another American soldier. This is the first time Colored ground troops have been used in combat in this theater. South Pacific Area, 4/6/1944" Co. K, 25th Regiment. Signal Corps Photo by Lt. Schuman. The GI is firing a M1 Garand rifle.

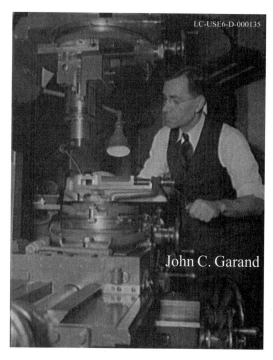

John C. Garand

Third Generation Blanchard Lathe made by the Onsrud Machine Works, Chicago, Illinois at the Springfield Armory. Note machined M1 Garand stocks in rack.

U.S. RIFLE, CALIBER .30 M1 — THE GARAND

Marine Corps Historical Center

Iwo Jima, February 1945. Initial wave landing on beach, Mount Suribachi in the background. Photo by Lou Lowery. The two Marines in center are carrying M1 Carbines.

U.S. CARBINE, CALIBER .30, M1 — THE M1 CARBINE

"Cpl. Robert Devin, Loberville, Texas and Cpl. Mark Drost, Daubaque, Iowa, U.S. Rangers covering French gun position captured by Rangers during early state of fighting for the Algerian harbor. 1st Ranger Battalion, Artew, Algeria 11/6/42". The Ranger in the foreground holds an M1 Garand rifle while the GI behind him is aiming a 1903 Springfield fitted with a grenade launcher.

THE 1903 SPRINGFIELD

"Infantrymen of Co. G., 415th Infantry Regiment, 104th Infantry Division, U.S. First Army take shelter behind a pile of rubble from a wrecked building in Cologne, Germany. 3/4/45". The GI on the left is carrying a BAR, at right center an M3 Submachine Gun with taped magazines.

SUBMACHINE GUNS

Naval Historical Center

Three Bluejackets practicing their marksmanship with Winchester Model 75 .22 caliber rifles. Note the aperture front sights — the initial purchases of .22 caliber training rifles retained civilian features such as aperture sights, high finish stocks and blued barrels — these expensive features were sometimes replaced by post front sights, linseed oil finished stocks and parkerized metal.

An important element of military training doctrine, marksmanship practice was viewed by most of the recruits, especially city kids, as one of the key steps in their becoming Soldiers, Sailors, Airmen, and Marines. The contributing author's father, Harry J. Davies lamented decades later that he was unable to go to the range at U.S. Naval Training Center, Sampson, N.Y. in upstate New York in the winter of 1944-45 — it snowed so heavily that the sailors were kept busy shoveling pathways in 10-foot high snowdrifts between buildings — training at the rifle range was cancelled.

.22 CALIBER TRAINING RIFLES

USAMHI

"Lt. Rene Liveben, Washington, D.C., Target Officer for the 63rd Infantry Division, U.S. Seventh Army looks at the four 20-mm cannon mounted in nose of destroyed ME262 jet propelled plane left on Reich Autobahn, used for landing after Allied planes bombed the airfield near Leipheim, Germany. 4/27/45". He carries only a holstered 45 Automatic pistol. Photographs of an unholstered pistol in the US Army Signal Corps collection are rare. This photo perhaps illustrates the subsidiary role of the pistol in World War II and the future of wars to come. The Nazi wonder weapons almost killed the author's Uncle Frank W. Green - a V-2 hitting a half block away while in London, England.

PISTOLS AND REVOLVERS

Marine Corps Historical Center

On Iwo Jima Corporals Charles A. Rich and Arthur R. Wack of 28th Marines, 5th Division. The Thompson is an M1 without its forearm. Above and behind their belt fed M1919 air cooled Browning machine gun is a 12 gauge "Trench" Shotgun, apparently a Winchester Model 12. Seemingly an anachronism in a machine gun pit — it could be used to deflect incoming grenades.

ACKNOWLEDGEMENTS

The following individuals provided invaluable assistance in the preparation for this work.

Randy Hackenburg	US Army Military History Institute		Dr. Roderick Speer, PHD - Editor
Jay Graybeal -	US Army Military History Institute		Frank Davies - Editor
Mark Wertheimer -	Naval Historical Center		Allen Cors
Ed Finney -	Naval Historical Center		Earle J. Coates
Lena Kaljot -	Marine Corps Historical Center		Lars Anderson
Charles W. Pate -	Uncle Joseph Green	Uncle Bill Miller	Harry J. Davies
Aunt Margaret Fox	Uncle Jack L. Fox Jr.	Christopher Litvinas	Thomas J. Green - Uncle Jack's son
Uncle Joseph T. Green	Uncle Frank W. Green	Uncle Bill Davies	John E. Green - Uncle Jack's son #1

"Wounded Marine proudly displays souvenir sword" Iwo Jima Feb 1945 — He also proudly displays his M1 Garand Rifle.

Marine firing Thompson M1 in taking of Wana Ridge, Okinawa. Photo by S/Sgt Kleine

INTRODUCTION

U.S Guns of World War II is based upon and uses the words and pictures from the *U.S Army Record of Army Ordnance Research and Development, Small Arms and Small Arms Ammunition* by the Office of the Chief of Ordnance, Research and Development Service, January 1946. Only 252 copies were initially distributed within the Army. New material has been added, primarily derived from official War Department reports and manuals. Also quoted from was *America's Munitions 1917-1918* by Benedict Crowell, Assistant Secretary of War, Director of Munitions, printed in 1919.

These reports give the United States Army's consolidated view of weapon development, research, and improvements to arms determined by field usage.

The original *U.S Army Record of Army Ordnance Research and Development* concentrated on M1 Rifle development showing the progress toward incorporating a 20 round 30-06 magazine — an arm that would have been fielded in 1946. It also heavily illustrated the arms tested in the development of the M3 Machine gun and the M1 Carbine. There was only minimal discussion of the 1903 Rifle, primarily centered on the adoption of the 03A4 Sniper Rifle. Likewise, Pistols and Revolvers were only lightly discussed. Shotguns were discussed only with a view to determining headspace problems. Training Rifles were totally ignored.

This book attempts to illustrate most of the shoulder and holstered small arms used by our GI's during World War II. An attempt has further been made to incorporate as many pictures of these arms in use as these pages will hold and to name the Soldiers, Sailors, Airmen, and Marines pictured when known.

Mention must be made of some of the books which collectors will find invaluable to determine models, variations, and rarity. Two books found most useful in arms identification were *U.S. Infantry Weapons of World War II* by Bruce Canfield and the superbly researched and flawlessly illustrated *U.S. Handguns of World War II* by my friend Charles W. Pate who graciously allowed me the use of numerous illustrations from his book. There are also a large number of excellent studies on individual arms listed in the bibliography.

Finally a few observations seem appropriate. Having written *C.S. Armory Richmond,* which details the history of a Civil War Armory, I was a bit surprised to see the same machinery, indeed some of the same Northern buildings being used to produce arms during World War II — notably, portions of the machinery to produce the M1903 Springfield dated back to before the Civil War. I also noted that the arms in production in 1941 and 1942 were the arms which fought the bulk of the war — most of the R&D efforts barely made it to the battlefield by war's end.

Marine Corps Historical Center

"Battle Remnants...Marine salvage crews collect lost and damaged weapons from a Guam battlefield and place them in piles." To the right of center is a solitary 1903 Springfield rifle — either a late issue arm or perhaps a survivor of the Marine defense of Guam in the early dark days of the war. The contributing author's Uncle William R. Miller, USMC was on Guam during its liberation in 1944.

FOREWORD

This book had its origins in research being done to complete *C.S. Armory Richmond* and a planned history of Harper's Ferry Armory for the years just before the Civil War. Searches of Army material documenting their early use of armory machinery caused me to find on a library shelf a rare copy of *U.S Army Record of Army Ordnance Research and Development* printed in 1946. The material, the record of research and primarily the illustrations were entrancing, and I felt a need to place the report before the general public so they too may enjoy reading and viewing the U.S. Army's efforts to improve the arms they supplied the GI during World War II.

Researching and writing my small portion of this book caused me to look back forty years to my youth when my Father and Uncles seemed so old to me — they had barely turned thirty and all were veterans of World War II. Not one of them would ever be heard discussing World War II at our picnics by the lake or at family get togethers. Only with the research to this book did I get a clearer idea of the part they played in that war. Hopefully, I'm excused for placing in several of the captions and in the dedication page brief pieces of information on the part they played in the great and horrendous struggle that was World War II.

Paul J. Davies

90th Infantry Division, 358th Regiment
21 January 1945, Luxembourg
Battle of the Bulge

Pfc. Virgil Morillison

USAMHI

81 mm Mortar observers
Sgt. Glen R. Maller carries an M1 rifle
in front of an abandoned Tiger tank.

USAMHI

Left — Pvt. Richard L. Turner, Co. "G," 23rd Infantry Regiment, 2nd Division holding a gas-trap M1. The batteries froze in the SCR-536 walkie-talkie held by Pvt. Lloyd Reed — 3/21/ 1943.

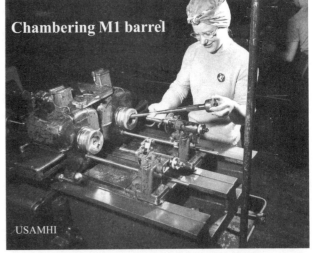

Chambering M1 barrel

USAMHI

M1 barrel being turned

USAMHI

U.S. RIFLE, CALIBER .30, M1 — THE GARAND

The basic models of practically all military rifles developed from 1900 to 1919 were in existence prior to 1900. These were the German Mauser, which probably exerted more influence than any other make, the Austrian Mannlicher, the British Lee-Enfield, and the French Lebel. In 1891 the United States tested and rejected the German Mauser of 1888 in favor of the Norwegian Krag-Jorgensen, and certain exclusive features relative to bolt action and magazine loading placed it among the best military rifles of that period.

U.S. Rifle, Caliber .30, M1903A1

In 1903 the United States adopted the U. S. Rifle, Caliber .30, M1903 (superseded in 1928 by the M1903A1 only differing from the M1903 Rifle in having a pistol grip stock), which was a modification of the improved Mauser Model of 1898. The influence of the Mauser improvement was clearly evident as no less than 26 nations either adopted the Mauser rifle directly or made only slight modifications in their own developments. Although the average barrel length of infantry and cavalry rifles was 30 inches, the U.S. Rifle M1903 for the purpose of standardizing on one service model, had a barrel length of 24 inches, and was equipped, with a 16-inch bayonet.

U.S. Rifle, Caliber .30, M1917

In 1914 the British Enfield Arsenal developed a Mauser type rifle which used .303 ammunition instead of .276 as originally intended, and the weapon was manufactured in the United States for the British. When the United States entered the war in 1917, a sufficient number of M1903 Springfields were not available, and since the British Enfield was already in production, the caliber was changed to .30-06, and several million of these rifles were produced for the American Expeditionary Force under the designation, Rifle, U. S., Caliber .30, M1917.

U. S. RIFLE, CALIBER .30, M1

While several attempts prior to World War I failed to produce a satisfactory semi-automatic shoulder rifle, in 1921 the United States sponsored a series of competitive tests in an effort to obtain a weapon having the following general characteristics: the rifle was to be of a self-loading type adapted to function with cartridges not less than .25 caliber or greater than .30 caliber, of good military characteristics, and preferably to fire the U. S. Cartridge, Caliber .30, M1906; it was to be simple and rugged in construction and easy to manufacture; furthermore, it was to require but little more attention than the regular service rifle when placed in the hands of the average soldier. More definite characteristics established were as follows:

a. The rifle was to be simple, strong, and compact. Weights to be well balanced and so placed that the essential strength was given to components requiring it. Ease of manufacture was to be the guiding factor in preparing the design.

b. The mechanism was to be well protected from the entrance of sand, rain, or dirt, and not to be liable to derangements due to accidents, long wear and tear, exposure to dampness, sand, etc.

c. Components of the mechanism were to be the fewest possible, consistent with ease of manufacture and the proper functioning of the weapon. Ready disassembly for cleaning purposes through the use of not more than one small tool, preferably the service cartridge, was required.

d. The rifle was to be so designed that the magazine, while in position in the rifle, could be fed from clips. The breech mechanism was to be so designed as to preclude the possibility of injury to the firer due to premature unlocking. The capacity of the magazine was not to exceed 10 rounds.

e. The firing mechanism was to be designed so that the firing pin would be controlled by the trigger and sear directly, that is, the bolt mechanism should move forward to the locking or firing position with the firing pin under the control of the trigger and sear mechanism so that the cartridge could not be ignited until the trigger released the firing pin.

f. The trigger pull, measured at the middle point of the bow of the trigger, was to be not less than 3 or more than 5 pounds.

g. An efficient safety or locking device was to be provided permitting the rifle to be carried cocked and with the cartridge in the chamber, without danger. The rifle was to remain cocked and ready for firing when the safety device was unlocked.

h. The weight of the rifle with magazine empty and without bayonet was to be a minimum, consistent with proper functioning, and in no case to exceed 10 pounds.

i. The rifle was to be designed to give good balance and be adapted to shoulder firing. Its general appearance and outline as nearly as practicable, was to be the same as the M1903 Rifle.

j. The rifle was to be strictly semi-automatic, its accuracy comparable to the M1903 Rifle; and the stock so designed, if practicable, to allow ventilation of the gun without charring or overheating the wood.

**Garand Primer Actuated
Semi-Automatic Trial Rifle**

**Thompson Caliber .30
Semi-Automatic Trial Rifle**

**Thompson Caliber .30
Semi-Automatic Trial Rifle**

Garand Semi-Automatic Rifle, Caliber .276

Pedersen Semi-Automatic Rifle, Caliber .276

Pedersen Semi-Automatic Carbine, Cal. .276

Garand Semi-Automatic Rifle, Caliber .30

TEST RIFLES

Among the various weapons submitted prior to and after the characteristics were established, were the .276 caliber Pederson semi-automatic rifle having a 24-inch barrel and a 10-round clip; the modified Bang semi-automatic rifle; the Berthier system rifle submitted by the United States Machine Gun Company which obtained its power from the expanding powder gases through a gas port in the barrel operating against a piston contained in a cylinder located underneath the barrel, the Garand semi-automatic rifle, caliber .276 having a tappet actuated in the bolt face and operating by set-back of the primer against the tappet; the Colt semi-automatic rifle, caliber ,30, delayed blow-back operation, and the Thompson auto loading rifle, caliber .30. Investigation was also made of the possibility of redesigning the M1903 Rifle to obtain the desired military characteristics as specified above. However, after due consideration this type of design was discontinued.

After considerable testing of the various rifles submitted, and necessary redesign of test models to a gas cylinder based design, the Garand semi-automatic rifle, caliber .30, was adopted by the U.S. Army in January 1936, as the U.S, Semi-automatic Rifle, Caliber .30, M1. During 1940 the gas port, cylinder, and other features were improved with certain modifications, and early in 1941, the U.S. Marine Corps adopted the Garand.

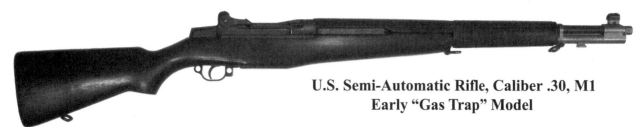

**U.S. Semi-Automatic Rifle, Caliber .30, M1
Early "Gas Trap" Model**

EARLY M1 PROBLEMS

The M1 rifle as initially produced utilized what is known the "Gas Trap" system to provide the gas to provide power to operate the rifle. This system was found unreliable as it allowed carbon buildup and had potential for allowing a cleaning patch to become stuck in the port. In addition, the barrel did not extend fully to the apparent muzzle of the rifle - a short false muzzle called a "gas plug" (drawing B8876, marked on part) provided what was found to be an insecure attachment point for the bayonet, Model 1910. Decision was made in late 1939 to replace the "Gas Trap" system with a "Gas Port" system, which was accomplished in 1940 by drilling a round hole in the underside of the barrel to provide gas to operate the mechanism. This change lengthened the barrel from 22 inches to 24 inches fully extending to the muzzle allowing a firmer bayonet mount. At the same time a compartment trap was added to the butt plate allowing storage of cleaning tools. A problem that had been observed in the first production arms, which caused "seventh round jamming", was resolved in 1940 by lengthening the receiver guide ribs. These early problems would lead directly to the great semi-automatic rifle controversy immediately before the beginning of World War II, just as production was reaching 1,000 M1 rifles per day at the Springfield Armory.

JOHNSON SEMI-AUTOMATIC RIFLE

The development of the Johnson semi-automatic rifle immediately preceding 1940 was another contribution in the field of semi-automatic rifles. Its semi-

**Johnson Semi-Automatic Test Rifle
Note use of Vertical Magazine**

automatic operation was by virtue of short recoil. Test of the Johnson rifle in 1940 resulted in the decision that the Johnson rifle, in spite of its alleged mechanical and manufacturing advantages, did not warrant further consideration as a replacement for the M1 Rifle. Later that year, the Netherlands - Indies Army adopted the Model 1941 Johnson, and some of these rifles were used in the southwest Pacific by certain units of the U. S. Marine Corps and the U.S. Navy.

**Also procured in small numbers was the
1941 Johnson Light Machine Gun**

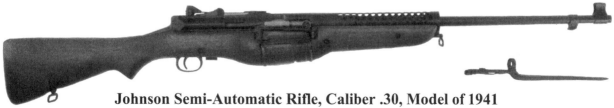

**Johnson Semi-Automatic Rifle, Caliber .30, Model of 1941
Note use of Rotary Magazine and light weight Spike Bayonet on Production Model**

M1 RIFLE FIELD DIFFICULTIES

In 1941 reports were received that difficulty was being encountered in the field when firing the M1 Rifle, due to jumping of the rear sight aperture. To overcome this defect, the rear sight nut was changed from a flush type to a wing type. This rear sight nut, B8877 (wing type or "Lock Bar) could be tightened by hand, thus overcoming the jumping difficulty. However, due to the construction of this nut it was possible, when it was carried on marches, for it to become unscrewed by the wing portion brushing against other equipment. This condition was aggravated by the fact that the rear sight pinion was too short and did not provide sufficient threads for the nut to rotate on. Shortly after this design of rear sight nut was received in the field, reports were received of excessive loss of the rear sight nut and other sight components. To overcome this serious defect, a new rear sight elevating pinion (C113698), having a longer threaded portion of sufficient diameter to permit counterboring and a new rear sight nut (B147799), threaded, to match the new pinion were developed and adopted in October 1942. A small staking tool was supplied with which to stake the pinion after assembly of the nut. When properly staked, the rear sight nut could be removed and replaced many times. This temporarily corrected the jumping of the rear sight aperture during firing, and eliminated the loosening of the sight and subsequent loss of components.

M1 RIFLE T105 REAR SIGHT

To fully overcome the various deficiencies, namely: loosening of components during firing and subsequent loss of components, hopping of the rear sight during firing and loss of small components due to disassembly of the sight for cleaning purposes, a project was

initiated to develop a sight having the following characteristics:

a. Application to the standard M1 Rifle without any modification to the rifle.
b. No hopping of rear sight during firing.
c. No loosening of sight components during firing.
d. Simplicity of design and operation.
e. Elimination of the use of lock nuts, peening, riveting, or spreading any portion of the sight, which would have to be disassembled for cleaning purposes.

In accordance with basic design features submitted by the Ordnance Department, Springfield Armory designed and fabricated pilot models of the T105 Sight, which met the above requirements. A minor modification of a retaining spring was suggested and incorporated in the T105E1 Sight. In this instance,

USAMHI

"WOW" using M1 barrel to gauge hand guard

the basic design of the standard M1 Sight was followed, but the components were grouped as two assemblies: the elevating knob and pinion assembly, and the windage knob assembly. Positive retention of the sight was accomplished by means of a Belleville type washer. As a result of the satisfactory performance in tests conducted by the Infantry Board, Aberdeen Proving Ground, and the Marine Corps Equipment Board, this new rear sight assembly was adopted in October of 1944, for complete replacement of rear sights on M1 Rifles manufactured to date, and for assembly to rifles in manufacture. At the close of the war complete replacement had not been effected.

"Lock Bar" Rear Sight Parts - from Left
- Elevating Knob Screw
- Elevating Knob
- Elevating Pinion
- Windage Knob
- Nut Lock Spring
- Nut Lock
- Rear Sight Locking Nut

T105E1 Rear Sight Parts Assemblies
Elevating Knob   Windage Knob

EXPERIMENTAL M1 RIFLE DESIGNS

During the course of the last four years (1941-1945), various investigations were conducted towards improvement of functioning of the M1 Rifle. In some instances, as will be seen, the application of new design in gun art, although not adapted for use on the M1 Rifle, proved satisfactory by test for possible future use.

In test firing of the M1 Rifle it was noted that under conditions of lack of lubrication, and under adverse conditions of rain, the action "froze" after a limited amount of firing. Various expedients in types of lubrication were tried and resulted in the adoption of a grease known as Lubriplate 130-A. The Lubriplate, when applied to the cam lug, the tang of the firing pin, underneath side of the bridge of the receiver, and the cam cut in the operating rod handle, allows the rifle to fire for longer periods of time under conditions of excessive rain or moisture.

In order to alleviate the condition of malfunctions in the rain, numerous attempts were made in the metallurgy of the lugs of the bolt to obtain a self-lubricating quality. These trials ranged from imbedding into the locking lugs of the bolt materials having a lubricating quality, and attempts to secure satisfactory performance by change in cam angles and surface finishes.

The use of a "free-floating" hammer proved effective in improving functioning in the rain; however, the resulting improvement was not sufficient to warrant incorporating the device in the M1 Rifle.

M1 Garand receivers being machined at the Springfield Armory. In 1944, 45% of the workers at Springfield Armory were women.

U.S. RIFLE, CALIBER .30, M1E1

Springfield Armory, at the direction of the Ordnance Office, fabricated test models of operating rod assemblies wherein a more gradual cam angle was machined in the operating rod handle. Tests of this item indicated that the "galling effect" as well as the "freezing" of the action were not materially improved.

U.S. RIFLE, CALIBER .30, M1E3

Further research to improve the functioning of the M1 Rifle resulted in the M1E3, wherein a roller lug was attached to the cam lug of the bolt and the cam angle in the operating rod handle was changed to match. Extensive rain tests conducted at both Springfield Armory and the Aberdeen Proving Ground indicated that rifles incorporating this design permitted from 25 percent to approximately 200 percent

M1E3

Standard M1

OPERATING RODS

M1E3

Standard M1

BOLT AND OPERATING ROD

Note Roller on M1E3 Bolt Locking Lug and Corresponding Cam in Operating Rod.

longer firing in the rain test than the standard M1 rifle. The duration of uninterrupted firing in both instances varied from gun to gun. Although the M1E3 Rifle showed superiority over the M1 Rifle, it was not recommended for adoption in view of the status of production of M1 Rifles in the middle of 1944. As a result of this satisfactory development, the roller lug design was adapted to the T20E2 Rifle (selective semi- and full-automatic fire), described in detail in a further portion of this record.

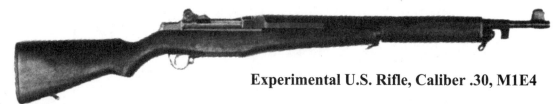

Experimental U.S. Rifle, Caliber .30, M1E4

U.S. RIFLE, CALIBER .30, M1E4

Further attempts to improve functioning of the M1 Rifle were directed towards increasing the dwell time and decreasing the velocity of the operating slide as it struck the cam lug of the bolt during the operating cycle. The thought behind this development was that an increase in dwell time would drop the residual pressure and a decrease in velocity would decrease the hammering or galling effect and that the combination of the two would permit smoother functioning. The M1E4 Rifle utilized a gas cut-off, gas expansion system wherein the gas port was located at approximately 8 inches from the muzzle. In this design the gas, after filling the expansion chamber, was cut off and allowed to expand. Immediately after the hammer reached the cocked position, the expanded gas was allowed to escape, thus the energy of the expanding gas was utilized until after the hammer was cammed downward by the approximately $4^{1}/_{2}$-inch rearward movement of the piston. Tests of the M1E4 Rifle compared to an M1 Rifle indicated that the dwell time was slightly more than doubled, the velocity of the slide at the time of impact with the

bolt was less than one-half; the velocity of the slide at its most rearward position was equal, and the overall time cycle was equal to that of the M1 Rifle. In this design, the gas being in contact with the piston for the complete time of the rearward cycle, an excessive heating of the operating rod and operating rod spring was produced.

USAMHI

M1 Garand stock being hand trimmed at the Springfield Armory. Note the Model 1903 rifle stocks in the rack, to the rear of the workman.

1. Bolt Assembly
2. Front Handguard Assembly
3. Front Sight Assembly
4. Main Assembly
5. Bracket, Gas Cylinder
6. Bayonet Base
7. Operating Rod and Piston Assembly
8. Gas Cylinder
9. Plug, Gas Cylinder
10. Follower Assembly
11. Operating Rod Springs
12. Stock Assembly
13. Trigger Housing Group

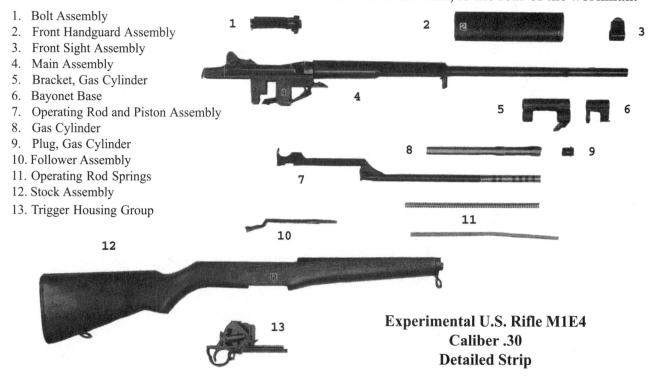

**Experimental U.S. Rifle M1E4
Caliber .30
Detailed Strip**

U.S. Experimental Rifle, Caliber .30, M1E9

"Maj. Gen. Jim Gavin CO of the 82nd Airborne Division, in front of the 3rd Battalion's command post on his recent tour of the front. 508th Infantry regiment 29 Dec 1944". All men from private to two star general carry the Garand.

U.S. RIFLE, CALIBER .30, M1E9

To eliminate the heating experienced in the M1E4 rifle, the M1E9 Rifle was developed. In this instance, a gas cut-off, gas expansion, long tappet principle was used wherein, the piston moved rearward approximately 1½ inches, the slide then completing its rearward stroke through inertia. All functioning results, insofar as timing was concerned, were equivalent to that of the M1E4 Rifle. Again the status of production of the MI Rifle did not warrant major redesign to incorporate this new gas system in the M1 Rifle, but the design is contemplated for use in a postwar development project of a new rifle.

USAMHI

1. Bolt Assembly
2. Handguard
3. Assembly Band
4. Front Sight Assembly
5. Main Assembly
6. Guide, Operating Rod
7. Pin, Operating Rod Guide
8. Gas Cylinder
9. Gas Piston
10. Bayonet Base
11. Plug, Gas Cylinder
12. Operating Rod
13. Follower Rod Assembly
14. Operating Springs, Inner and Outer
15. Stock Assembly
16. Trigger Housing Group

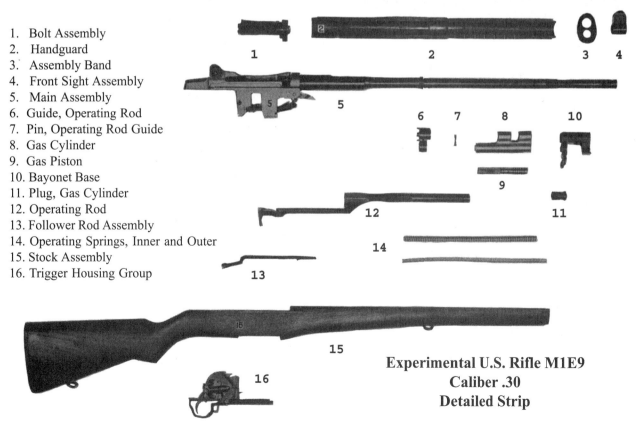

**Experimental U.S. Rifle M1E9
Caliber .30
Detailed Strip**

U.S. Rifle, Cal. .30, M1E5
Stock in Extended Position
(Note attached M15 Grenade Sight Mounting Plate)

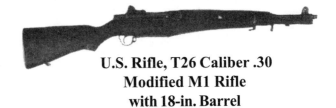

U.S. Rifle, T26 Caliber .30
Modified M1 Rifle
with 18-in. Barrel

EXPERIMENTAL RIFLE, U.S., CALIBER .30, M1E5

Reports from combat theaters up to 1944 indicated the desirability of developing a short, light weight, folding stock, M1 Rifle. Springfield Armory was directed to fabricate a test model wherein the barrel was to be 18 inches long, and a folding stock similar to the stock of the M1A3 Carbine (pantograph type) was to replace the standard stock. Tests at the Aberdeen Proving Ground indicated that the accuracy for ranges up to 300 yards was comparable to the M1 Rifle, but that the blast and flash were excessive. Informal opinions of Headquarters, Army Ground Forces indicated the need for a partial or full pistol grip on the T6 Stock for the M1E5 Rifle; however, the development of the item was to be carried at a low priority. In view of the priority of other development items at Springfield Armory, the improved Stock T6E3 was not completed.

EXPERIMENTAL RIFLE, U.S., CALIBER .30, T26

In July of 1945, the Pacific Theater requested that they be supplied with 15,000 short M1 Rifles for Airborne use. A design of short M1 Rifle was delivered to the Ordnance Department by a courier from the Pacific Warfare Board, A comparative study of the sample short M1 Rifle and the M1E5 Rifle indicated a definite preference for the M1E5 action equipped with the standard stock; the rifle so assembled was designated as T26. A study by Springfield Armory resulted in a tentative completion schedule of 5 months for the limited procurement of 15,000 T26 Rifles; however, with the occurence of V-J Day on 14 August 1945, this requirement was dropped.

Note: A number of M1 rifles have been altered to the T-26 configuration, and are known as "Tanker" Garands. All have commercial origins.

USAMHI

September 9, 1944

"39th Regt., 9th Inf. Division advances into a Belgian town under protection of a heavy tank."
Left soldier has a BAR, others carry M1 Garands. The Sherman tank has a hedgerow cutter.

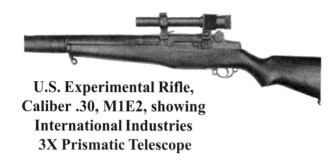

**U.S. Experimental Rifle,
Caliber .30, M1E2, showing
International Industries
3X Prismatic Telescope**

EXPERIMENTAL RIFLE,
U.S., CALIBER .30, M1E2

At the time that Headquarters, Army Ground Forces recommended the standardization of the M1903A4 Sniper's Rifle, it was also recommended that the M1 Rifle be equipped with a telescope in such a manner as to permit clip loading and normal functioning of the weapon. This development was attacked from two angles, namely: the use of a prismatic type telescope off-set to the left with the eyepiece piece centered, and a straight type telescope, left side mounted, and utilizing an adjustable cheek pad.

The designation M1E2 was assigned to the M1 Rifle equipped with the prismatic type telescope and dovetail mount as developed by the International Industries. Based upon the results of a test by the Infantry Board of this item and an M1 Rifle equipped with an M73B1 Telescope and Stith type mount, Headquarters, Army Ground Forces made the following recommendations:

a. No further consideration be given to the above two items.
b. That the mounting of the telescope be modified as follows:

(1) So as to lower the telescope to bring the optical axis as nearly as practicable on a level with the standard iron sights when set for medium ranges.

(2) So as to bring the axis of the telescope as nearly as practicable to the vertical plane through the axis of the bore and still permit clip loading.

(3) So as to bring the rear end of the telescope forward to a position one-quarter inch in front of the forward edge of the elevation knob on the iron sight.

(4) So as to permit fore and aft adjustment of the telescope tube of at least one-half inch to fit the conformation of the individual.

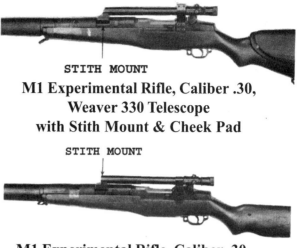

STITH MOUNT
**M1 Experimental Rifle, Caliber .30,
Weaver 330 Telescope
with Stith Mount & Cheek Pad**

STITH MOUNT

**M1 Experimental Rifle, Caliber .30,
Weaver 330 Telescope
with Stith Mount & Mount Plate**

c. Consideration be given to the substitution of a rear sight similar to the ramp-type sight on the M1903A3 Rifle for the present standard M1 Sight on all M1 Rifles, modified for use as sniper's rifles.
d. That an adjustable cheek pad be supplied with M1 type sniper's rifles.

RIFLE, U.S. CALIBER .30, M1E6.
(NOT ILLUSTRATED)

A drawing study was initiated to determine the advisability of developing a left side mounted telescope and utilizing a ramp-type rear sight similar to that of the M1903A3 Rifle in order to permit usage of the iron sights with the telescope in position on the rifle. This study resulted in the decision that the M1E6 Rifle of this design would be undesirable from the standpoint of the extensive M1 Rifle receiver modifications.

Marine of 51st Composite Battalion placing 8-round clip into M1 — the fingers are in front of slide to avoid a "Garand" thumb.

Camp Lejeune March1943

Library of Congress

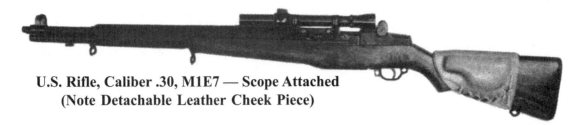

U.S. Rifle, Caliber .30, M1E7 — Scope Attached
(Note Detachable Leather Cheek Piece)

SCOPED RIFLES
U.S., CALIBER .30
M1E7 AND M1E8 RIFLES

In order to conform with the recommendations of Headquarters, Army Ground Forces, two sniper's rifles were developed and submitted for test. The M1E7 Rifle incorporated a dovetailed cam operated pressure plate type of mount (Griffin & Howe design), while the M1E8 Sniper's Rifle (Springfield Armory design) incorporated a block-type mount attached to the chamber end of the barrel. The M1E7 type mount required the drilling and tapping of three holes and the drilling of two tapered holes in the left side of the receiver. The M1E8 type mount required a machined block pinned to the chambered end of the barrel and a shortened rear hand guard. In both instances the M73 or M73B1 Telescopes were to be used. Each type of rifle was supplied with the T2 Cheek Pad which was constructed of leather and included a lacing to fasten it to the stock. A choice of three thicknesses of cheek pad could be secured to the leather base by means of snap fasteners. Simplification of the T2 Cheek Pad included elimination of the snap fasteners and the addition of three thicknesses of felt increments which were secured by lacing. Thickness adjustment was obtained by removal or insertion of increments. This design of cheek pad, designated T3, was later redesigned to accomplish retention of the felt increments and the cheek pad on the stock by means of one instead of two lacings. This item carried the designation of T4. A duplication of the leather T4 Cheek Pad was produced from polyvynol chloride as a substitute for leather and designated as T5.

On the Springfield Armory design of Sniper's Rifle M1E8, a cork covered metal adjustable Cheek Piece T6, was assembled to the stock. After informal tests by Headquarters, Army Ground Forces, more face support was added to the cheek piece in the model designated as T6E1; however, in the later part of October 1944, it was recommended that no further consideration be given to this item.

On the basis of Infantry Board Tests of the M1E7 and M1E8 Rifles, the M1E7 Rifle equipped with a $2^{1}/_{2}$ -power telescope was standardized in June of 1944, as U. S. Rifle, Caliber .30, M1C (Sniper's), thus making the M1903A4 Sniper's Rifle Limited Standard. In order to assure production meeting requirements, the M1E8 Rifle was adopted in September 1944 as a Substitute Standard and designated as U. S. Rifle, Caliber .30, M1D (Sniper's). The Leather

M1 Garand barrel bore being gauged using a Precisionaire air gauge by a Woman Ordnance Worker at the Springfield Armory. She wears a red and white WOW bandana, for safety.

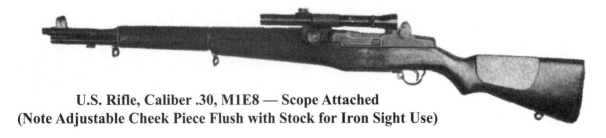

U.S. Rifle, Caliber .30, M1E8 — Scope Attached
(Note Adjustable Cheek Piece Flush with Stock for Iron Sight Use)

**U.S. Rifle, Caliber .30, M1C
with Hider, Flash, M2**

Cheek Pad T4 was adopted for use on both the M1C and M1D Rifles in October 1944.

A combination Rain and Sun Shield T6 for the objective end of the telescope, and a protective rubber Eye-piece T5E1 on the ocular piece were adopted for use with the M1C and M1D Rifles in January 1945.

For purposes of proper identification, the M73 Telescope with cross wire type reticule, equipped with a rubber eyepiece and rain-sun shield (Drawing Number 91-246), was designated as Telescope M81, and the M73 Telescope with tapered post type reticule, equipped with a rubber eyepiece and rain-sun shield (Drawing Number 91-247) was designated as Tele-

M1 Garand barrels being reamed at the Springfield Armory by a teenaged apprentice.

**82nd Airborne Division, 80th Antitank Bn., "prior to going into battle"— Neuville, Belgium 12/29/ 1944 — from left: Pvt. Charles Beadeux, Cpl. Theodore Sohoski and Pvt. John Bogdan.
All carry M1 Garands and prayers into battle.**

scope M82. A cone type Flash Hider T18, designed to attach to the M1C and M1D Rifles by means of the bracket assembly of the M7 Grenade Launcher and capable of eliminating approximately 90 percent of the flash at 100 yards, was adopted as an accessory to the sniper's rifle in January 1945, and designated as Hider, Flash, M2.

**U.S. Rifle, Caliber .30, M1D
Only experimental M1D Rifles were produced during World War II.
Most would be assembled during the Korean War.**

1. Collimator Sight T53
2. Instrument Light T12

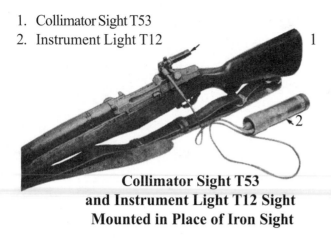

**Collimator Sight T53
and Instrument Light T12 Sight
Mounted in Place of Iron Sight**

COLLIMATOR SIGHTS — (INFRARED)

At the request of Headquarters, Army Ground Forces, as a result of the Infantry Board test of an exploratory model of a Collimator Sight T53 with Instrument Light T12, a project was initiated in September 1944 to develop a collimator sight for night use with the M1C and M1D Sniper's Rifles.

This sight, designated as Sight, Reflex-Collimator, T110E is currently in process of completion. This sight embodies the following features and characteristics:

    a. Attachable to the M1C and M1D Sniper's Rifles by the same type of mounts.

    b. Suitable for either day or night use because of a self-contained electrical system employing two dry cells (T110 Sight employed one dry cell), electric bulb and a switch rheostat.

    c. Contains a light beam reticule, dot and circle type.

    d. Contains a view plate, on which the light beam reticule is reflected and transparent so that the eye which sees the reticule also sees the target and permits a field of view of 6 degrees plus.

    e. Contains elevation and windage adjustment with micrometer click graduations in yards for elevation and minutes of angle for wind age.

Realizing that deterioration of batteries in storage and frequent replacement of batteries are objectionable features, a development is under way to attempt to overcome the necessity for the use of batteries. Recent developments in materials and technique of application indicate the possibility of illuminating reflex-collimator sights by natural light in daylight hours, and by radium activated phosphorescent ma-

Woman Ordnance Worker (WOW) operating turret lathe on breech of a M1 Garand barrel at the Springfield Armory. She wears a red WOW bandana — with white ordnance bombs.

terials during periods when insufficient natural light is available. This development to effect illumination of sights of the T110 type is being carried under the designation of Sight, Reflex-Collimator, T140.

Further investigation of collimator type sights for replacement of iron sights for daytime use is being carried on in the Sight, Reflex, T131. This item embodies a concave transparent lens of small diameter and a reticule fixed in proper relationship to the curvature, both mounted on a base plate. This item will be readily adaptable to any small arms weapon by means of mounts appropriate to the type weapon with elevation and windage adjustments as required.

**U.S. Rifle, Caliber .30, M1C with
Sight Reflex — Collimator T110**

**(Note that same Mount is used for Scope
and Collimator Sight)**

Magnesium Stock, Rifle, T9

MAGNESIUM RIFLE STOCK, T9

From time to time during both World War I and II the probability of a scarcity of black walnut blanks for rifle stocks existed. During this past war the use of both cherry and birch woods was authorized as a substitute for black walnut. In the fall of 1944 it was deemed advisable to investigate the possibility of the use of light alloys for rifle stocks. Although this project was not in itself urgent, it was desirable, in view of the nonuniformity in weight and grain structure of wood, the occasional difficulty in obtaining proper black walnut blanks, the increase in strength of alloy stocks and the possible decrease in weight of alloy stocks. Accordingly, a contract was placed with the Light Metal Alloy Foundry, State College of Washington, for the development and fabrication of a cast magnesium alloy stock for the M1 Rifle.

In fabricating the T9 Stock, some troubles were encountered in surface shrinkage, but this was overcome by applying corrective foundry methods. Clean up and machining offered no difficulties. In firing tests made at the facility there was no noticeable tendency for the metal stock to transmit noises or vibration of firing to the ear. Explosion of firing seemed normal and the same as for the wood stock. The resulting weight of the stock was equal to the wood stock but this weight could be decreased through the use of permanent mold methods to effect thinner sections rather than the sand casting methods employed. The theoretical strength of the T9 Stock up to the yield point is four times the strength of the wood stock at the most critical location, the neck. The center of gravity is shifted rearward somewhat. Eighty shots fired as rapidly as clips could be inserted, caused no uncomfortable heating of the metal stock.

Should further investigation of a light metal alloy stock be indicated, it might be pointed out that a resinous coating should be applied to insulate the metal to make it more comfortable to handle in winter weather. Quantity production of the stock might be achieved by the permanent mold method of fabrication. Two or more stocks could be set in one mold and the baked sand core could be set in. the usual fashion. It is also possible that this type of stock, might be made as a die casting, but this would likely be feasible only after considerable study and investigational work is done.

FIELD REFINISHING PAINT FOR THE GAS CYLINDER

Early production gas cylinders for the M1 Rifle were coated with a finish known as "Molyblack." Continuous use of the rifle resulted in a shiny gas cylinder. A paint known as Stoner-Mudge was authorized for field service application to such gas cylinders. In order to find a superior field refinishing paint, Springfield Armory conducted a long series of tests of the following types of refinishing paints; Stoner-Mudge S-12801, DuPont PI00-P-4425, Egyptian K-67225, Zapon Air Dry S-551, Zapon Bake-S-551, Egyptian K-76895, Pittsburgh VC 30065, Pratt and Lambert No. 37, Murphy Flat Black Lacquer, Du Pont P100-P-4486, Du Pont P100-4487, Pratt & Lambert No. 39, Egyptian AXS-821, Jones-Dabney ES 680, Class 215, Murphy Air Dry Flat Black, Egyptian K77031, Hilo ES-680 Class 215, Stoner-Mudge SX-1697, Kemick No. 11, Stoner-Mudge (1 quart of S-1281 thinner with 2 ounces USA Spec. 3-176).

The various materials were applied with a brush and air-dried and baked. The tests consisted of wear and air-dry abrasion, high temperature exposure, high temperature and wear tests, alkali resistance, resistance to vapor degreasing, resistance to dry-cleaning solvents, thermal shock reflectivity, and hot oil immersion.

Results of this extensive test indicated that Du Pont P100-P-4486 was preferred as either an air-dry or baked-on paint. This paint was further improved by Du Pont by a better blending of pigments and vehicle and a slower drying time. The improved paint, P100-P-9562-S-1, was authorized on 1 April 1944 as a preferable paint to Stoner-Mudge S-1281. The Aberdeen Laboratory, Springfield Armory and Du Pont coordinated in preparing a suitable specification for this material.

In the interim, as a result of the above described tests, Field Service, Maintenance, published TB-23-5-6, dated 5 June 1944, pertaining to instructions for application of a flat black paint 52-P-270 (formerly known as Stoner-Mudge No. S-1281) thinned with synthetic enamel thinner 52-P-441-75, in the ratio of 2 ounces thinner to 1 quart of paint for an oven-baked finish until suitable specifications of the preferred type could be made available.

FINISHES PERTAINING TO FACTORY APPLICATION ON STAINLESS STEEL GAS CYLINDERS FOR THE M1 RIFLE.

During the period of manufacture of the M1 Rifle, various types of finishes were used on stainless steel gas cylinders. The first, approximately, 500,000 rifles made had gas cylinders finished with "molyblack." It is definitely known that these cylinders became shiny. Springfield Armory converted to the use of Dichromate Black, and Winchester Repeating Arms Company to Iron Plate and Dulite. Rock Island Arsenal, in connection with overhaul and repair work used a Black Chromium finish. Gas cylinders, with these various finishes were not identifiable and therefore no definite conclusion could be reached as to the superiority of one over the other in field usage.

Springfield Armory was directed to make wear tests of gas cylinders coated with the various materials referred to above, plus experimental finishes. All testing was done on a Taber Abraser Machine using CS-15 Calibrase Wheels with a 500-gram load on each head. The following finishes were tested and the corresponding cycles represent the number of cycles required to wear away the finish from 50 percent of the surface of the abrasion track:

Armor Vit .... 1800-1850 cycles
Parco Lubrite and
    Dubian Black .... 1650-1950 cycles
Parco Lubrite (baked one-half hour
    at 350° F) .... 1,000 cycles
Armory Dichromate .... 500 cycles
Zinc Base Parkerite (baked one-half hour
    at 350° F) .... 200-300 cycles

In view of the favorable results obtained in previous tests of M1 Rifle gas cylinders coated with AV-164 Black Armor Vit under laboratory conditions, a week's trial production (consisting of approximately 15,000 gas cylinders) of this method for blackening stainless steel cylinders was made by the Armory Manufacture Department. Careful observations were made during the process of application of this finish to determine its desirability as a production method.

At the conclusion of the week's trial production the satisfactorily coated Armor Vit cylinders were assembled to M1 Rifles. Serial numbers of these rifles were recorded, together with the type of finish applied to the cylinder. Twenty-five hundred rifles,

M1 Gas Cylinder

each with Armor Vit and Dichromate coated cylinders were shipped to Camp Blanding, Florida, and to Camp Croft, South Carolina, respectively, for field testing. All cylinders coated with Armor Vit were marked with the letters "VX" for identification. No serious difficulties were encountered during this production trial in the application of Armor Vit. A clean, grit-blasted surface free from contamination is of prime importance for the proper adherence of the coating to the base metal. Close control of coating thickness is necessary to maintain dimensional tolerances and to prevent blistering m the baking cycle.

Although the comparative abrasion tests made of these Armor Vit coated cylinders indicated that they possessed better resistance to wear than cylinders finished with Dichromate black, extensive field tests will be the determining factor. In laboratory tests Armor Vit coatings show evidence of moderate brittleness on sharp impact.

Co. E., 11th Regt.
5th Division
3rd Army
1945

Courtesy John E. Green

"A Kraut plane near Plattlin, Germany"

His standing squadmate carries a M1 Garand rifle on top of the wing of a German FW-190. The other two arms seen are also M1 Garands.

"Credited with shooting 25 Japs with his BAR during the attack of Oct 21, 1944. Leyete P.I.". Pfc. Henry J. Latanski, 3rd platoon, Co. L, 34th Inf. Regt., 24th Infantry Division with his BAR.
Photo by Pvt. Daniel Eiaman

DEVELOPMENT OF SELECTIVE SEMI- AND FULL-AUTOMATIC RIFLES BASED ON THE DESIGN OF THE M1 RIFLE.

The light automatic weapon normally carried as a squad or section weapon was the Rifle, Automatic, Caliber .30, Browning, M1918A2, familiarly known as the BAR.

The principal characteristics of this weapon place it in a medium weight class since, complete with bipod and magazine, its weight is 19.4 pounds. It is gas-operated and air-cooled, with a magazine capacity of 20 rounds. The rate of fire is variable, there being a slow rate of 300 to 350 rounds per minute, and a fast rate of 500 to 600 rounds per minute. Originally designed as a shoulder operated rifle, it has had many modifications, nearly all of which increased its weight and length. In the early part of 1944, consideration was given to the possibility that a weapon of the BAR type, but lighter and having more modern characteristics, might be required. Initially, Springfield Ar-

mory and Remington Arms Company were directed to develop a paratrooper's rifle having the following characteristics:

a. Weight—9 pounds complete, less magazine.
b. Over-all length in closed stock position—26 inches (Use of a flash hider should be thoroughly investigated in connection with shortening of the barrel)
c. Magazine clip—20 rounds.
d. Bipod equipped.
e. Semi-automatic fire on closed bolt.
f. Full-automatic fire on open bolt.
g. Suitable for launching grenades with stock in open position.
h. Use standard M15 Grenade launcher Sight.

Insofar as possible it was requested that all of the above characteristics be accomplished with a minimum change in tooling of the M1 Rifle, and that such deviations from standard components used in the M1 Rifle were to be simple in design and ease in manufacture.

The rifle under development at Springfield Armory was designated as Rifle, Caliber .30, T20, and that at Remington Arms Company as Rifle, Caliber .30, T22.

Further investigations to cover the approach to possible solution of design problems included continued development of the Johnson Light Machine Gun, and the offer of a development contract to the Winchester Repeating Arms Co. Division of Western Cartridge Company in connection with the above type of design, previously suggested, which they carried on under their own expense.

Johnson Light Machine Gun
Model of 1944

10 Were Procured
For 1945 Army Tests

The Johnson Light Machine Gun represents a form of design based on recoiling barrel operation with magazine feed, and conforms in general to the requirements for a squad or section weapon.

29

81st Infantry Division — original caption reads "Anguar, D plus 3 & 4, Sept. 1944"
GIs on left and right carry M1 Garand rifles. Center GI has a Browning Automatic Rifle.

M1 Garand barrels being proof stamped
at the Springfield Armory.

M1 Garand rifles being assembled
at the Springfield Armory. The calendar reads
16 April 1943.

USAMHI

Infantrymen of the 5th Infantry Division crossing the Moselle River 8 September 1944 in a combat boat. They are carrying M1 Garand .30 caliber rifles. The contributing author's Uncle, Sgt. John E. Green, Company "E", 5th Infantry Division, 11th Infantry Regiment participated in the crossing of this river. The unit would suffer over 50% casualties by V-E Day. Uncle Jack was wounded two times, once remaining a week in a coma, always being returned for duty. He received the Bronze Star for gallantry.

Reports from combat theaters and personnel returning from overseas stressed the continued requirement for efficient, automatic small arms of light weight. The comparatively heavy Browning Automatic Rifle, Caliber .30, M1918A2, had proven to be an effective and efficient automatic weapon. Likewise, the Rifle, Caliber .30, M1, as a semi-automatic weapon, had proven itself superior to any rifle used by our allies or enemies. In view of these conditions. Headquarters, Army Ground Forces, in September 1944, stated that a requirement existed for a weapon similar in efficiency, size, and weight to the M1 Rifle, and lighter in weight than the Browning Automatic Rifle, which by means of a change lever could be used

as a semi-automatic or full-automatic weapon. It was further requested that the following developments be initiated:

a. That the present Rifle, Caliber .30, M1 be modified to include automatic features which will enable the operator to select and fire the weapon either as a semi-automatic or automatic piece.

b. That such automatic fire by means of a light bipod be equally as effective as the standard Browning automatic rifle, as concerns dispersion, cone of fire and ballistic characteristics.

c. That the mechanism be simple and capable of field stripping, with operative features which would reduce stoppages to a minimum.

31

d. That a suitable 20-round bottom feed magazine and a detachable bipod mount be developed for this weapon.

Accordingly, both Springfield Armory and Remington Arms Company were instructed to change the original specifications on both the T20 and T22 Rifles, respectively, to eliminate the requirement for a folding stock and short barrel, and to substitute therefore a straight stock with as high comb and standard barrel length of the M1 Rifle, equipped with front and rear sights.

U.S. Rifle, Caliber .30, T23

RIFLES, CALIBER .30, T23 AND T24

In order to evaluate the preliminary design to effect selective semi- and full-automatic fire, the Remington Arms Company completed two models of rifles, one incorporating the selective fire control by means of independent hammer release and designated as Rifle, Caliber .30 T23, and the second model having selective fire control by means of independent sear release and designated as Rifle, Caliber .30, T24. Both models performed satisfactorily in Remington tests prior to delivery to the Ordnance Department. The T23 model was preferable from the standpoint of design, durability, and minimum of functional stresses. It fired full-automatic from an open bolt approximately 20 percent of the time. It could be made to fire 100 percent from an open bolt by a simple change in timing, but in such a design an element of danger existed as the arm would fire when the operating handle was moved forward manually, as would occur when feeding cartridges which were slightly deformed or which failed to seat home for various reasons, thus resulting in a badly bruised hand. Consequently, this design was not recommended. Simplification of the T23 design, by removal of a major component and several minor components to permit the weapon to fire full-

automatic from a closed bolt, eliminated this hazard. The T24 model was preferable to the T23 if minimum time to produce and minimum conversion costs to the standard M1 Rifle were to be the primary considerations, for the T24 fired full-automatic from a closed bolt at all times. In both the T23 and T24 the 8-round "enbloc clip" was used for preliminary tests. The T24 model was equipped with a straight high comb stock, but informal firing of this model indicated that there was no appreciable value insofar as muzzle climb was concerned, to warrant consideration of a deviation from the standard M1 Rifle stock to a straight stock.

Tests of the T23 model conducted at the Aberdeen Proving Ground in the early part of November 1944, confirmed opinion as to desirability for firing from the closed bolt position, as well as the desirability of designing a new magazine rather than attempting to modify the Browning automatic rifle magazine. In all instances wherein the BAR magazine was used, considerable battering of the magazine was experienced by virtue of the material used in this magazine, because of its over-all design. The general functioning of the weapon was satisfactory, showing that the basic principle of operation was sound. The difference between the straight and standard stocks was not sufficient to determine effect on accuracy. A device designed to increase gun stability during automatic fire was definitely needed. This information was transmitted to Remington Arms Company in order to incorporate the necessary changes in the T22 Rifle having the basic design of the T23 Rifle, but incorporating all of the design requirements as stated above.

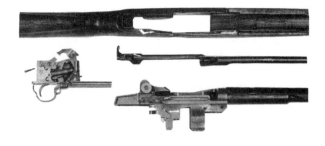

U.S. Rifle Caliber .30, T23 - Field Strip

(Note Modified Stock, Operating Rod, New Components on Receiver and Modified Trigger Mechanism)

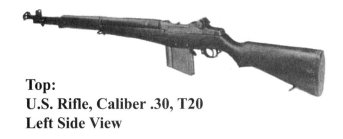

Top:
U.S. Rifle, Caliber .30, T20
Left Side View

Bottom:
U.S. Rifle, Caliber .30, T20
Right Side View

U.S. RIFLE, CALIBER .30, T20

Early in November 1944 Springfield Armory delivered to the Aberdeen Proving Ground the first model of the T20 Rifle, wherein selective semi- and full-automatic fire was accomplished by means of independent sear release actuated by a connector operating off of a cam on the operating slide during the last free forward movement of the slide after the bolt was in the locked position. Here, again, the 20-round capacity BAR magazine was modified. In this design an attempt was made to have automatic fire from an open bolt, and semi-automatic fire form a closed bolt. Since, as in the Remington model, this feature was not dependable, it was eliminated.

The gas cylinder was locked into position with a recoil check or muzzle break, which greatly reduced the shock of recoil and prevented the rifle from

"climbing" during full-automatic fire, but this device did not permit mounting a bayonet, grenade launcher, or flash hider. Results of Aberdeen Proving Ground tests indicated the need for an improved magazine as well as better magazine retention in the weapon. It was concluded that the basic principle of operation was satisfactory, the recoil reducer greatly aided gun stability during automatic fire, that feed failures were principally due to battered and deformed magazines; and that minor design changes and strengthening of various components should be made.

U.S. RIFLE, CALIBER .30, T20E1

The T20E1 Rifle, incorporating the changes desired as a result of testing previous models, fired both automatic and semi-automatic from a closed bolt, omitting the unsatisfactory feature for holding the bolt open on automatic fire and substituting in lieu thereof two heat flow arresting grooves on the barrel before the chamber for chamber cooling. In addition, the receiver was further modified to simplify, the operation of locking the receiver and trigger group together as well as to introduce a more secure means of lock-

U.S. Rifle, Caliber .30, T20E1

U.S. Rifle, Caliber .30, T20
Major Groups

U.S. Rifle, Caliber .30, T20E1
Major Groups

U.S. Rifle, Caliber .30, T20E1

ing the box magazine within the magazine well. At the same time, the receiver was prepared to mount a telescopic sight, night sight, or grenade launcher sight, as might be desired. The recoil check was modified to take a bayonet. However, the T20E1 Rifle was still incapable of mounting a grenade launcher or flash hider. A new box magazine to replace the modified BAR magazine was developed to work in conjunction with the new method of locking in the receiver and this magazine provided the only means holding the bolt to the rear in its retracted position. This magazine was not interchangeable for use in the BAR.

The T20E1 Rifle mounted an adjustable bipod from the gas cylinder but this bipod was not readily removable.

During the period of 22 through 26 January 1945, the T20E1 Rifle was tested at the Ordnance Research Center, Aberdeen Proving Ground. This model was complete in all details, and the test results, other than the failures to feed, were exceptional. These failures to feed were caused by the bolt bearing surface in the barrel being soft. The following minor changes and improvements were authorized to be incorporated in the 10 Rifles T20E1 to be fabricated for service test:

   a. Induction harden the breech end of the barrel.
   b. Increase length of the bipod to permit greater command height.
   c. Redesign the gas cylinder and gas cylinder lock screw assembly to permit ready attachment and removal of rifle accessories.
   d. Improve the hand guard to prevent charring.

In view of the favorable test results and simplicity of design of the T20E Rifle, Springfield Armory was instructed to fabricate 100 models incorporating the above changes for extended service test. This definitive design was designated as Rifle, Caliber .30, T20E2.

Further tests of the T20E1 Rifle by the Infantry Board and the Marine Corps Equipment Board resulted in the incorporation in the T20E2 Rifle of the following improvements:

   a. Magazine to be usable in the BAR.
   b. Magazine catch to be altered in shape to eliminate the possible hazard of being accidentally depressed or damaged during rough handling.
   c. Provision of means for retaining the operating slide in the rear position in order that the rifle might be cleaned in the prescribed manner.

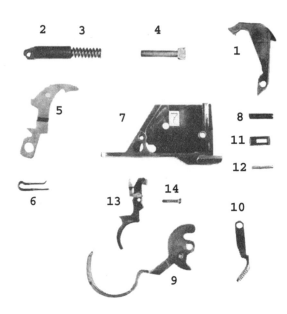

U.S. Rifle, Caliber .30, T20E1
Disassembled View of Trigger Mechanism

1. Hammer
2. Housing, Hamper Spring
3. Spring, Hammer
4. Plunger, Hammer Spring
5. Safety
6. Ejector, Clip
7. Housing, Trigger
8. Pin, Hammer
9. Guard, Trigger
10. Catch, Magazine
11. Bushing
12. Spring, Magazine Catch
13. Trigger and Sear Assembly
14. Pin, Trigger

"Gauging the diameter of the barrel of a Garand rifle following grinding" at Springfield.

M1 Stocks being finish filed by a hand stocker.

"First rough cut has been made in these rifle stocks as they take shape from the blank"

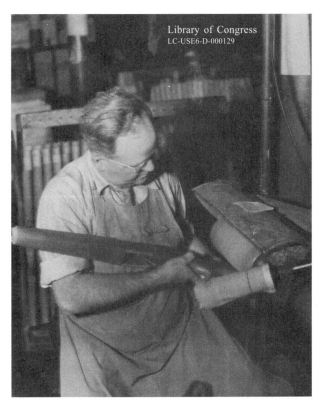

M1 Garand stock being finish sanded at the Springfield Armory.

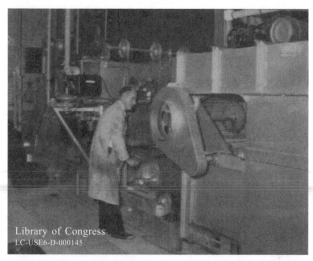

Heat treatment machine at Springfield Armory.
Note linked conveyor belt to worker's right.

"Worker inspecting bore of a complete barrel for
a Garand rifle" at the Springfield Armory.

"Garand rifles being packed for shipment."

Broaching machine being used in manufacture
of the Garand at the Springfield Armory.

Assembling Rifles at the Springfield Armory.

The pictures of the manufacture of the M1 Garand at the Springfield Armory on this and the preceding page were photographed in September 1940 by Alfred T. Palmer for the Farm Security Administration.

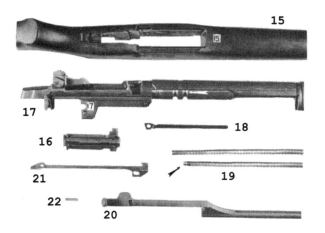

**U.S. Rifle, Caliber .30, T20E1
Disassembled View of Stock
and Receiver Components**

15. Stock Assembly
16. Bolt Assembly
17. Main Assembly
18. Guide, Operating Spring
19. Operating Rod Spring
20. Operating Rod
21. Connector
22. Connector Spring

U.S. RIFLE, CALIBER .30, T20E2

The T20E2 Rifle developed from its predecessors, the T20 and T20E1 Rifles, is gas-operated, air-cooled, and fed from a 20-round box magazine which is inserted in the bottom of the rifle. Like the T20 and T20E1 Rifles, the T20E2 Rifle can be fired either semi- or full-automatic at will. Full-automatic fire is achieved by means of a connector assembly, which, when moved into engagement by the operator, is actuated by the operating rod handle, and in turn actuates a sear release or trip which, with the trigger held to the rear, disengages the sear from the hammer lugs immediately after the bolt is locked. With the connector assembly moved out of engagement by the operator the rifle can be fired only semi-automatically and functions the same as the M1 Rifle. The T20E2 differs from the T20EI Rifle mainly in the recoil check, bolt and receiver. The recoil check has been further modified to permit the mounting of a special flash hider and a new type grenade launcher as well as a bayonet. The recoil check and grenade launcher, together with a new valve, are so designed as to permit semi- and full-automatic firing of ball ammunition or AP cartridges without the removal or manual adjustment of the launcher by the firer. An improved bipod with longer; legs is readily attachable to the recoil check. The bolt has been slightly modified to ease feeding and extraction. Also, the roller lug feature of the M1E3 Rifle bolt has been adopted, and with this addition, the weapon's performance in rain has been greatly improved. The receiver of the T20E2 Rifle is slightly longer than that of the M1. This allows the bolt to travel farther to the rear and improves feeding.

The receiver has had its bridge modified to mount an operating rod lock to hold the bolt open when so desired for cooling or cleaning.

Many other changes have been incorporated which greatly facilitate assembly and operation as well as simplify manufacture, it should be noted that many of the changes in this category have been applied to the original T20E1 Rifles. Connector and connector spring have been riveted into a permanent assembly with the addition of a connector spring guide, operating rod spring guide lengthened, magazine latch and release mechanism designed to facilitate one-hand removal of magazines and simplification of over-all design. The magazine has been further modified to be serviceable in the Browning Automatic Rifle. It must be noted, however, that the reverse is not possible. Browning Automatic Rifle magazines will not function in the T20E2 Rifle.

Model designation and serial number of the rifle are stamped on the receiver directly back of the rear sight.

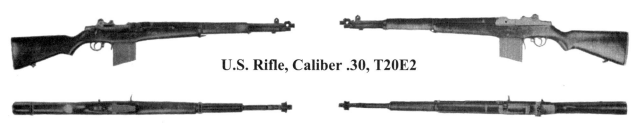

U.S. Rifle, Caliber .30, T20E2

Right Side and Bottom Views   **Left Side and Top Views**

Courtesy John E. Green

Photo of S/Sgt. John E. Green (right) and members of his squad carrying M1 rifles in front of the remains of a Nazi ME-262 jet. The squadron markings indicate the ME-262 was part of Jagdgeschwader 7 "Nowotny".

Pertinent Data:
Weight of gun without accessories—pounds…9.63
Weight of accessories—pounds
    20-round magazine (empty)...............0.55
    Flash hider ....……0.28
    Grenade launcher ....…0.47
    Bipod ....Not available
    Bayonet, M1905.................…………1.12
    Bayonet, M1 ....……1.0
    Sling, M1907 (leather).......................0.5
    Sling, M1 (web)...............…………...0.26
    Grenade Launcher Sight (M15) with
        Adapter........................0.25
    Telescopic sight and mount
      (with Telescope, M82)...................1.18
    Combination Tool M3 or M3A1...........0.22
    Oiler and Thong Case (metal)
        complete..............................0.24
    Oiler and Thong Case (plastic)
        complete………..................0.10
    Grease container (full)......................0.02
Length over-all without bayonet—inches........44.88

Length over-all with Bayonet, M1—
inches....54.75
Length over-all with Bayonet, M1905, in. 60.95
Length over-all with flash hider attached........48.13
Length over-all with grenade launcher attached
        inches..........................48.88
Length of barrel—inches..............................23.70
Rifling:
    Length—inches 21.00
    Number of grooves................................4

**U.S. Rifle, Caliber .30, T20E2
Disassembled**

Twist—direction ....Right hand
Twist—inches 1 turn..............................10
Operation ....Gas
Feed ....Box magazine
Rate of fire—shots per minute:
    Automatic 700
    Semi-automatic…..Limited by dexterity of
        operator
Capacity of feeding device—rounds. 20
Weight of feeding device loaded—pounds........1.69
Sights:
    Maximum graduated range—yards....1,200
    Sight radius—inches......27.9 for 100 yards
Trigger pull, minimum and maximum-pounds..
        Not determined
Cooling ....Air
FM No. ....23-5, TB No.9X-l15

U.S. Rifle, Caliber .30, T20E2

**Left Mechanism
in Semi-Automatic Position.**

**Right Mechanism
in Automatic Position**

In order to expedite supply of T20E2 Rifles to the using arms in combat theaters, Ordnance Committee action was taken in May 1945 recommending that the Rifle, Caliber .30, T20E2, be designated as Limited Procurement Type, and that 100,000 of these items, together with spare parts and accessories, be procured on a high priority, reducing correspondingly the quantity of M1 Rifles to be manufactured under the current Army Supply Program. However, due to the cessation of hostilities on 14 August 1945, this requirement was eliminated and authorization was granted for completing fabrication of the original 100 models.

Ten T20E2 Rifles were completed in July 1945 and seven were submitted to Aberdeen Proving Ground for test. Test results indicated that two components required further development, these being the recoil check and the hand guard. With the recoil check the blast on the ears of the firer was objectionable. The objection to the hand guard was that sustained firing caused it to heat excessively with subsequent charring of the wood.

Completion of the balance of 90 rifles is being held in abeyance pending completion of the design of definitive types of recoil check and hand guard to overcome the above deficiencies, as well as for the completion of a suitable grenade launcher, flash hider, and bipod.

U.S. Rifle, Caliber .30, T22
Closeup of Receiver Components

These modifications were included in the T22E1 Rifle, and based upon the successful Proving Ground test of this model, Remington Arms was authorized to complete three models of the T22E2 type of rifle which would incorporate a slight change in the trigger group to simplify manufacture as well as disassembly and assembly, plus a magazine catch more readily usable, and the use of the same design of gas cylinder, gas cylinder valve screw assembly, recoil check, flash hider, and bipod, as that to be used on the T20E2 Rifle.

The design of the T22E2 Rifle, it is believed, is such as to more readily lend itself to remanufacture of M1 Rifles as a peace time operation by virtue of the use of the standard length M1 receiver, rather than an increased length receiver such as is used on the T20E2 Rifle.

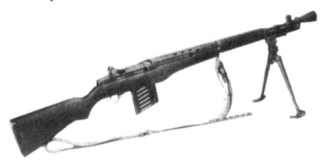

U.S. Rifle, Caliber .30, T22

RIFLE, CALIBER .30, T22, T22E1, AND T22E2

To retrace our steps in this record, Remington Arms Company continued development of the T22 types of rifles. The T22 type of rifle, after test, required minor modifications to improve functioning and usability of magazine release and retention of the bolt in the open position.

U.S. Rifle, Caliber .30, T22E1

(Note Bipod Legs in Position, Sling, Magazine, Muzzle Depressor, and Shoulder Rest)

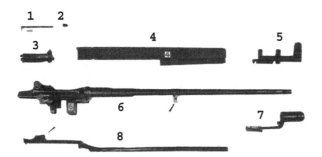

**U.S. Rifle, Caliber .30, T22E1
Showing Modified Parts**

1. Spring Loaded Firing Pin
2. Modified Extractor
3. Bolt
4. One Piece Hand Guard
5. Modified Gas Cylinder
6. Receiver—Note Bolt and Operating Slide Guide
7. Muzzle Depressor
8. Modified Operating Slide— Note Built-up Area

WINCHESTER AUTOMATIC RIFLE

Ten models of the Winchester Automatic Rifle were purchased for test purposes. The design of these guns was undertaken by Winchester without a Research and Development Order. The design is a complete departure from the M1 Rifle and utilizes the essential design characteristics of the carbine.

These weapons were distributed to Ordnance Agencies for inspection and study, to the Ordnance Research Center, Aberdeen Proving Ground, to the Infantry Board, and the Marine Corps Equipment Board for such tests as they deemed advisable.

Rifle, Caliber .30, Winchester

**Three Quarter View
Showing Bipod, Sling, Flash Hider, and
Shoulder Support**

For comparative purposes, the following tabulation of weights and dimensional characteristics of the Browning Automatic Rifle, the M1 Rifle, and the T20E2 Rifle is made:

	Browning Automatic Rifle	M1 Rifle	T20E2 Rifle
Gun (stripped)	16 lb. 10 oz.	8 lb. 12 oz.	9 lb. 10.1 oz. includes recoil reducer
Recoil Reducer	None	None	3.5 oz.
Bipod	2 lb. 5 oz.	None	1 lb. 2.5 oz.
Magazine	8 oz.	Clip 1 oz.	8.8 oz.
Sling (leather)	8.7 oz	8.7 oz.	8.7 oz.
Weight, complete w/ fully loaded magazine			
	21 lb. 3 oz.	10 lb. 1 oz.	13 lb. .3 oz.
Magazine	20-round	8-round	20-round
Over-all length	47.72 in.	43.6 in.	44.9 in.

BROWNING AUTOMATIC RIFLES

The M1918 Browning Automatic Rifle, which has been used extensively from the time of its adoption up until June 1937, was superseded by the M1918A1 model at that time.

The M1918A1 model is the basic gun equipped with bipod, mount, and a hinged butt plate. The stock on the automatic rifles supplied for use with hinged butt plate, and the butt plate assemblies are not interchangeable with the early models, and therefore the A1 designation was adopted in order to provide for proper description of this item in standard publications.

When the M1918 model was approved for reclassification as obsolete (July 1945), provision was made that all subject items available were to be converted to the M1918A2 model. The component parts of the M1918A1, being used in manufacture of the M1918A2 units, it was deemed advisable, especially in view of the small number of M1918A1 models in existence, to reclassify this design as obsolete, thus leaving only the M1918A2 as the standard item.

"B.A.R."

**Browning Automatic Rifle
Caliber .30, M1918**

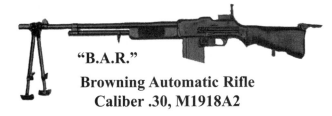

"B.A.R."
Browning Automatic Rifle
Caliber .30, M1918A2

PLASTIC STOCK FOR B.A.R.

Reports were received early in 1942 to the effect that many Browning Automatic Rifles required replacement of stocks due to breakage. This breakage was usually due to cracks developing on the right and left sides opposite the center line of the buffer mechanism recess. To overcome this difficulty with wood stocks, a thermo-setting plastic using chopped fibers of cloth as a filler was developed. The ease with which a plastic of this type could be molded allowed a much higher rate of production than could be obtained with wood stocks. The cost differential between the two, if any, was very small.

Aberdeen Proving Ground reports on tests of plastic stocks for the Browning Automatic Rifle indicated that such a stock is superior to the wood stock in strength and ability to withstand shock at both high and low temperatures.

Since the Browning Automatic Rifles were being used to a greater extent than ever before, the need for a sturdy, easily manufactured stock to replace those wood stocks broken in service was very urgent. Hence the plastic stock for the M1918A2 Browning Automatic Rifle was adopted in March 1942.

The type of construction in the plastic stock did not lend itself to the incorporation of an oiler or thong inserted into the stock through the butt plate, as the oiler and thong would be difficult, if not impossible, to remove for use, and in any event would be held loosely within the stock.

The buffer and rate reducing mechanism used on the Browning Automatic Rifle being only adjusted or removed from the stock by removing the stock from the receiver and removing the screw from under the butt plate, the stock did not therefore require a butt plate trap. Therefore, the butt plate trap for the Browning Automatic Rifles was eliminated as of October 1942.

CARRYING HANDLE FOR B.A.R

In an effort to improve the handling characteristics of the Browning Automatic Rifle, development of a simple handle readily attached to the rifle in the field was initiated in October 1943. Of the several designs produced, the most successful one was developed by Springfield Armory and consisted of two steel stampings suitably formed and held in position on the barrel by two screws. A stout wooden handle shaped to fit the hand, and provided with a stop to prevent the hand from touching hot metal, slips over the body of the handle. It can be assembled to rifles in the field without requiring special tools. This design, with some slight modifications to increase its strength, was recommended for adoption by Headquarters, Army Ground Forces, as a result of Infantry Board tests (Infantry Board Report Number 1696). The Handle, Carrying, T4 was adopted as auxiliary equipment for the M1918A2 Browning Automatic Rifle in December 1944.

Uncle Jack's Buddies & his old B.A.R.

The 1918A2 B.A.R. Uncle Jack carried across France has no flashhider or bipod and the forearm is broken. Note the worn parkerizing on the magazine. Hoiman carries a M1 Garand. Picture taken with a captured 35-mm Leica camera.

Courtesy John E. Green

Co. E., 11th Regt., 5th Division, 3rd Army

"Whitie and Hoiman in Ervzen, Germany halfway through the Seigfried line. Whitie with my old B.A.R. and his own top hat. Feb. 45".

Infantrymen of 90th Infantry Division, 358th Regiment take advantage of the Maginot line to protect themselves from small arms fire. From left: James Grontage holds M1 carbine, L.B. Fields an M1 rifle, Willard Budrug an M1 rifle and 1st Lt. Charles Hammock an M1 carbine.

Men of 24th Infantry Division, 34th Infantry Regiment looking over Jeep captured by the Japanese. Leyete, Philippines — October 1944. Photo by Robert J. Sorace

Collection of Earl J. Coates

M1 Carbine manufactured by Quality Hardware

U.S. CARBINE, CALIBER .30, M1 — THE M1 CARBINE

DEVELOPMENT OF THE CARBINE, CALIBER .30

During World War I all officers, many noncommissioned officers, and the enlisted personnel of such organizations as ammunition trains and Signal Corps units were equipped with the Caliber .45 Pistol M1911, later slightly modified and redesignated M1911A1. This weapon was primarily for defensive purposes since its effective range is limited to not more than 25 yards, except when handled by an expert; its ineffectiveness was well proved by the amazingly small number of casualties inflicted upon enemy troops during World War I as revealed by postwar inspection of German casualty lists and hospital records.

While the exact form of an intermediate weapon between the standard pistol and the infantryman's rifle was not established during the years following World War I, it was agreed that the need called for a semi- or full-automatic weapon, more accurate, possessed of longer range, and with a higher fire potential than the caliber .45 pistol.

Appropriations for the development of ordnance materiel were very limited during these years, and consequently no action was taken on the suggestion of the Chief of Infantry, in September 1939, to initiate a project for the development of a light rifle to be used by ammunition carriers. The consensus was that such personnel could be equipped with the service rifle (M1), and that the advantages of the lighter weapon would be outweighed by complications attending the design and manufacture of both the weapon and a new cartridge.

The success of the German Wehrmacht subsequent to the invasion of Poland in September 1939, prompted further action on this matter, and on 15 June 1940, the Chief of Infantry restated our need for a light rifle capable of semi- or full-automatic fire. With the German technique as an example of effectiveness, the restatement of the need for such a weapon was extended to include in addition to ammunition carriers, machine gunners and mortar crews, whose positions might be endangered, and administrative and communications personnel attacked by parachutists or ground forces which had penetrated our defenses. On the same day, 15 June 1940, the Secretary of War issued orders for the development of such a weapon, and this action authorized the Ordnance Department to set in motion the machinery of design, development, test, and eventually manufacture.

After certain basic requirements for both the gun and its cartridge had been established, a circular was prepared and forwarded to the following recognized small arms manufacturers and inventors:

1. Auto Ordnance Company
2. Colt Patent Firearms Company
3. High Standard Manufacturing Company
4. Harrington and Richardson Arms Company
5. Johnson Automatics, Inc.
6. Marlin Firearms Company
7. J. D. Pedersen
8. Remington Arms Company
9. Savage Arms Company
10. Smith & Wesson Company
11. Winchester Repeating Arms Company

Springfield Caliber .30 Light Rifle

Auto-Ordnance Light Rifle Caliber .30

Right View in Position Ready to Fire

Right Side View

During the next few months this circular was mailed to other corporations and individuals until approximately 25 had been notified of the War Department's requirements.

The gun was to weigh not more than 5 pounds. The action was to be semi-automatic with a selector to permit full-automatic fire. Magazines were to be of 5-, 10-, 20- and 50-round capacity, the latter for full-automatic firing. The mechanism of the gun was to be protected against the entrance of sand, rain, and dirt, and be able to function.

A standard testing program was adopted, and designers and manufacturers were advised of the requirements for the competitive basis upon which all weapons would be received.

The rifle was to be weighed and notation made of the name and number of all parts and the number and types of springs used in its assembly.

The time required for field stripping and for complete disassembly and reassembly of the rifle was to be recorded.

Endurance tests required the firing of 4,500 rounds semi-automatic and 500 rounds full-automatic. All stoppages, malfunctions, breakages, and replacements were to be recorded.

The standard dust test was defined as exposing the weapon, magazine empty, to an agitated mixture of road dust and dry cement. The magazine was then to be loaded with clean cartridges and firing attempted. The test was to be repeated with the magazine fully charged before exposure to the dust.

The testing board was authorized to inaugurate any other tests, which might be considered necessary or desirable in determining the relative merits of the weapons submitted.

Auto-Ordnance Light Rifle, Caliber .30 Right Side View, Field Stripped

**Bendix No. 3
Light Rifle
Caliber .30**

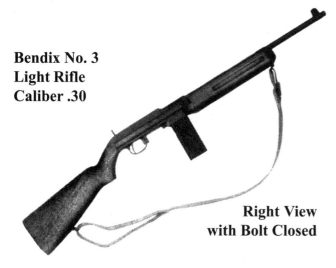

**Right View
with Bolt Closed**

**Savage Caliber .30
Light Rifle**

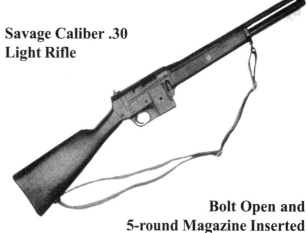

**Bolt Open and
5-round Magazine Inserted**

A subcommittee was appointed of representatives of each of the interested service forces, and of the Technical and Industrial Service Divisions of the Ordnance Department. This committee was made responsible for the test program and the selection of the rifle which most nearly met the requirements.

The date on which all entries were to be submitted was finally set as 1 May 1941. On that date nine rifles were presented to the subcommittee in Washington. Two were eliminated without further consideration, the first of these being a rifle with a straight blowback action submitted by Mr. C.E. Simpson of Springfield Armory. This weapon was considerably overweight, and the inventor stated that the weight could not be reduced below 6 pounds. The second was the White, Caliber .276, gas operated rifle, sub-

mitted by Dr. Kohler and Mr. John J. Murphy. This weapon was offered only to suggest a possible design for a light rifle, and no effort had been made to meet the established requirements. The remaining seven entries with the dates set for tests were as follows:

Organization	Inventor	1941
Auto Ordnance Co.	Mr. Bergman	May 22, 23, 24
Bendix Aviation Corp.	G. J. Hyde	May 29, 30
Colt Patent Firearms		
Mfg. Corp.	V.A. Browning	May 15, 16, 17
Harrington & Richardson		
Arms	E.C. Reising	May 19, 20, 21
Savage Arms Corp.	J. Pearce	May 8, 9, 10
Springfield Armory	J.C. Garand	May 26, 27, 28
Woodhull Corp.	F. W. Woodhull	May 12, 13, 14

It should be noted here that at the time the original proposals were submitted by the Ordnance Department, the Winchester Repeating Arms Company was engaged in educational production of the Garand (M1) rifle along with other experimental work for the Ordnance Department and was therefore unable to enter the competition.

The seven rifles to be tested showed some possibilities of meeting the requirements, but five exceeded the 5-pound weight limit. After some discussion the board concluded that 5 pounds was a rather drastic limitation, and consequently the permissible weight was increased to 5° pounds including sling and 5-round magazine. Some of the rifles exceeded even that limit, but their inventors claimed that weights could be reduced in time for tests; the later dates being assigned to those having the most difficult changes

**Harrington & Richardson
Caliber .30 Light Rifle**

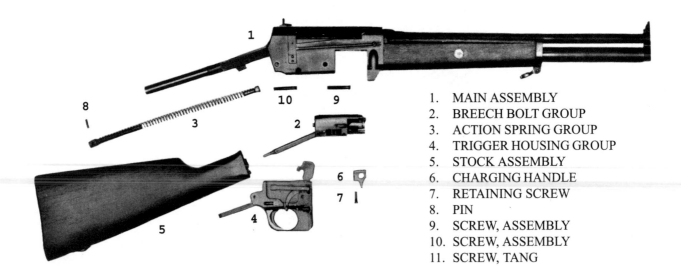

1. MAIN ASSEMBLY
2. BREECH BOLT GROUP
3. ACTION SPRING GROUP
4. TRIGGER HOUSING GROUP
5. STOCK ASSEMBLY
6. CHARGING HANDLE
7. RETAINING SCREW
8. PIN
9. SCREW, ASSEMBLY
10. SCREW, ASSEMBLY
11. SCREW, TANG

Savage Caliber .30 Light Rifle - Right Hand View, Field Stripped

to make. However, the rifle submitted by the Colt Patent Firearms Manufacturing Company was not ready on the date assigned. A new date was allowed, but the manufacturers were unable lo get the weapon to function to their satisfaction, and it was withdrawn from the competition.

The test program to be conducted at the Aberdeen Proving Ground was amended to provide the assignment of a recorder to each rifle. The recorder would remain with the rifle throughout each test and would be responsible for such data as number of rounds fired, number and nature of malfunctions and breakages, and the description of all necessary repairs and of parts replaced. Inventors were notified that flash, accuracy, recoil, velocity, and high- and low-angle firing would be included in the program.

The manufacturers were required to have a qualified gunsmith present throughout the tests of their rifles. These gunsmiths were permitted to make adjustments when necessary and replace broken parts. Any part replaced was to be of the same design as that originally incorporated in the rifle. Only such minor changes were permitted as an alteration in the angle of a bearing surface or the use of a larger, hardened pin or screw to replace one which had worn excessively during the tests. Neither the gunsmiths nor the other representatives of the manufacturers were permitted on the firing lines or to examine any rifle other than their own.

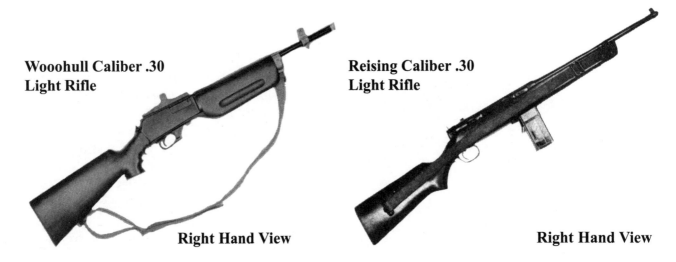

Wooohull Caliber .30 Light Rifle

Reising Caliber .30 Light Rifle

Right Hand View

Right Hand View

A table of values was prepared as a standard by which the entries could be compared one with another.

Weight	15 points
Length	10 "
Simplicity	15 "
General functioning	25 "
Endurance	10 "
Accuracy	5 "
Recoil	5 "
Rain-Dust test	5 "
Unusual positions	5 "
Hand operation	5 "

100 points

**Garand Caliber .30
Light Rifle**

Left Hand View

It was necessary to allow second tests to the Savage Arms Company, the Auto Ordnance Corporation and the Bendix Corporation; and second and third tests to the Woodhull Corporation. The additional time was required to manufacture new parts to replace those broken during the first tests. The overall results of these tests were, for various reasons, unsatisfactory. Since the chief objections of the inventors centered in the fire control mechanism, the carbine subcommittee decided that full-automatic fire would not remain a requirement. Accordingly, the revised specifications indicated that the proposed rifle should be designed to fire semi-automatic only.

Prior to July 1941 the, Winchester Repeating Arms Company had developed a 7° pound, caliber .30 experimental rifle from an early model Winchester self-loading sporting rifle which used .32 Winchester blowback rifle loads. The results of privately conducted Winchester tests on the experimental rifle favorably impressed the Ordnance Department. Winchester also felt that by utilizing the basic ideas in this rifle they could design a 5-pound weapon, which would handle a considerably smaller caliber .30 self-loading (SL) Cartridge.

Winchester, aided by suggestions of Ordnance Department personnel, fabricated a sample gun which weighed only 5 pounds and offered good possibilities, although the preliminary firing showed that the

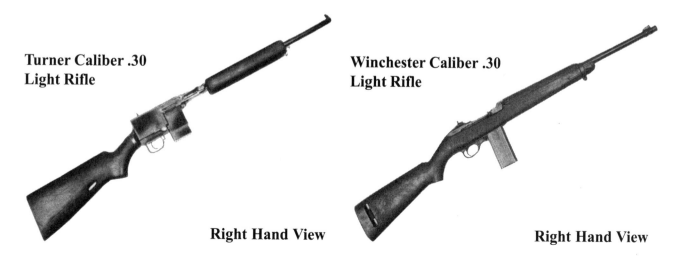

**Turner Caliber .30
Light Rifle**

Right Hand View

**Winchester Caliber .30
Light Rifle**

Right Hand View

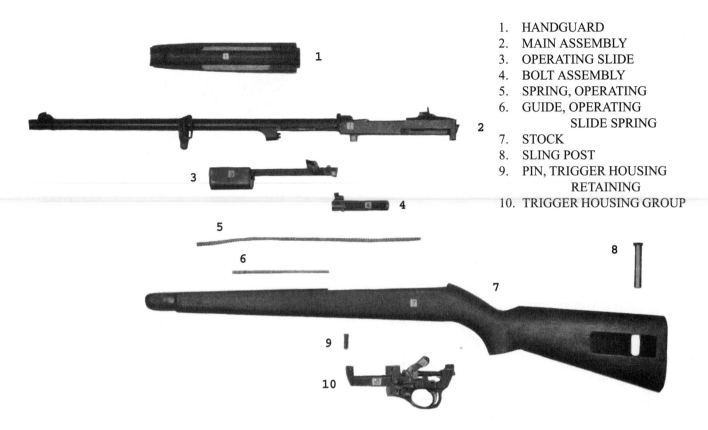

1. HANDGUARD
2. MAIN ASSEMBLY
3. OPERATING SLIDE
4. BOLT ASSEMBLY
5. SPRING, OPERATING
6. GUIDE, OPERATING SLIDE SPRING
7. STOCK
8. SLING POST
9. PIN, TRIGGER HOUSING RETAINING
10. TRIGGER HOUSING GROUP

Winchester Caliber .30 Light Rifle — Left View, Field Stripped

gun did not function reliably. After the gun was test fired on 11 August 1941 at the Aberdeen Proving Ground, the Ordnance Department requested Winchester to make any necessary modifications to attempt elimination of various malfunctions, and submit the improved model for the general competitive tests scheduled for 15 September 1941.

In order to give Winchester ample time in which to redesign and fabricate the improved model, the deadline for submission to test was advanced one full day, thus allowing the Ordnance Department time to fire the gun 1,000 rounds before submitting it to the test board.

The gun was delivered to the Ordnance Department at Aberdeen on time, and it negotiated the 1,000-round preliminary test with but one stoppage. It was submitted to the dust test, was photographed, and test data accompanied the reports. The following morning the gun was entered in the active competition, and 3 days later the field had only two competitors, namely, a carbine designed at Springfield Armory and the Winchester model. Subsequently the Winchester model became the unanimous choice of the test board.

CHARACTERISTICS

The U. S. Carbine, Caliber .30, M1, is a gas-operated, self-loading shoulder weapon delivering semi-automatic fire from a box magazine of 15-round capacity. General functioning is similar to that of the U. S. Rifle, Caliber .30, M1. As the bullet traverses the barrel a portion of the propellant gas passes through a port located approximately 4.5 inches forward of the chamber. The pressure of the gas in the gas cylinder drives the piston back 0.140 inch, and this rearward movement is transferred to the operating slide which carries the bolt with it to the rear. The slide travels approximately 0.3125 inch when its force is transmitted to the bolt cam lug. The delay involved prevents opening of the bolt until the bullet has left the barrel and dangerously high pressures have subsided.

A camming action rotates the bolt slightly which disengages the locking lugs, and starts extraction of the fired case before the rearward movement is begun. This slight rotation also initiates recocking of the hammer, and cams the nose of the firing pin away from the primer of the fired case. The bolt moves to

Iwo Jima Beachhead. Marines dig in under Japanese fire. Mount Suribachi looms at right.
February 20th 1945. The Marine in foreground laid his M1 carbine on Iwo's black volcanic sand.

Marine Navajo Code Talker on Iwo Jima.
He carries a M1 Carbine.

Marines climbing down nets for invasion of
Tarawa. All carry M1 Carbines.

USAMHI

"Placing shoes and clothes in mule bags. Italy 1943."
Note the folded M1A1 Carbine on seat of this 45th Division Jeep.

5/11/45   Marine Historical Center

"Okinawa...Machine gun crew moves up."
Center crewman carrying M1917 Browning
machinegun tripod also carries an M1 Carbine.

(Right) Marines on Guam unloading a 75MM
Pack Howitzer from a DUKW. The Marines
on the "Duck" all carry M1 Carbines.

the rear, extraction is completed and the empty case ejected, the hammer is cocked, and the operating spring is compressed to furnish the power required for the forward (counterrecoil) movement of the slide and bolt.

On the return stroke the bolt picks up the top cartridge from the magazine, and pushes it into the chamber. The camming action, mentioned above, is reversed and the bolt is rotated into its locked position. Premature firing is prevented by a slot in the receiver bridge in which the tang of the firing pin must engage before the pin can move forward in the bolt to firing position. This mating cannot be accomplished until the bolt completes its rotation to the locked position. The weapon is then ready for firing, after which the cycle is repeated.

In the event of failure of the self-loading mechanism, the gun may be operated as a hand-operated repeating weapon, the slide being retracted by hand and released.

In October 1941, approval and standardization of the Carbine, Caliber .30, M1, by the Secretary of War and the Adjutant General was received and read for record as OCM 17360.

The first model guns, fabricated by the Inland Manufacturing Division, General Motors Corporation, Dayton, Ohio, were subjected to a 5,000-round endurance test at the Springfield Armory. In this test difficulties developed in extraction and ejection. Work was immediately started to correct these malfunctions. Subsequently, other deficiencies were found in the bolt holding plunger, sight setting, and magazine catch. Developmental work for the correction of malfunctions and deficiencies was to be carried on as a continuous project, and for this purpose Aberdeen Proving Ground and Springfield Armory each received, about January 1942, 10 carbines of Inland manufacture for inspection and tests.

Subsequent to the tests at Springfield Armory, Infantry Board tests of early production carbines also noted deficiencies in the trigger group of the carbine, namely, excessive trigger pull, and malfunctions. Both Winchester Repeating Arms Company and Inland Manufacturing Division of General Motors Corporation investigated new designs of the trigger group as well as simplification for manufacture from the standpoint of design and materials used.

CARBINE, CALIBER .30, M1E1

Two improved models of carbines designated as M1E1 were fabricated by Winchester and subsequently tested at Aberdeen and studied by Inland with a view to still further simplifying manufacture and improving functioning. The trigger pull averaged about 6 pounds, which was a considerable improvement over the standard carbine. The Inland design of trigger group for lighter trigger pull involved a new hammer, sear, sear spring, hammer spring, and hammer spring plunger for replacement as a group in the standard carbine. Extensive tests showed that the trigger pull was maintained between $4\frac{1}{2}$ and 6 pounds) with a maximum increase of $\frac{1}{4}$ pound during a 10,000-round endurance test.

At the suggestion of Industrial Division representatives, a new hammer and hammer spring, to accomplish lighter trigger pull, in place of the five components developed by Inland, were tested. Both the hammer and hammer spring were interchangeable in all carbines either individually or as a group. With these components, the trigger pull varied from 4° to $6\frac{1}{2}$ pounds.

Both Aberdeen Proving Ground and Inland tested 12 and 10 sets respectively, with satisfactory results. In view of the interchangeability features of these two components into existing carbines they were approved in May 1943 for production as part of the Carbines, Caliber .30, M1, M1A1, and M1A2, in lieu of the corresponding items, and sufficient quantities were to be produced for replacement in all carbines in service.

CARBINE, CALIBER .30, M1E2

To permit early production of the carbine after its standardization, a rock-over type sight was authorized until a satisfactory adjustable rear sight could

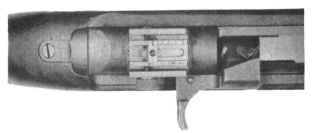

U.S. Carbine, Caliber .30, M1
Showing Experimental
Adjustable Rear Sight T21

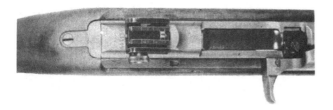

**U. S. Carbine, Calibre .30, M1
with M1A2 Adjustable
Rear Sight Mounted—Top View**

The Carbine, M1E2, with the special receiver to accommodate the T21 Sight modified in accordance with the above was standardized in January 1943 as Carbine, Caliber .30, M1A2, thus making the M1 Carbine Substitute Standard. In view of the urgent requirement for carbines, the changeover to produce the M1A2 Carbine in place of the M1 Carbine could not be made without materially affecting production. Because of this, further development resulted in the modification of the T21 Sight to permit its use on all Carbines, Caliber .30, M1 and M1A1 in the process of manufacture and in the hands of troops. The adoption of this sight, Ordnance Department Drawing No. D73955, resulted in the obsoletion of the Carbine, Caliber .30, M1A2, in November 1943.

be developed. Inland Manufacturing Division of General Motors Corporation, in the later part of 1942, developed a ramp-adjustable sight designated as T21. This required a modified carbine receiver to obtain the proper rear sight elevation setting, and subsequently lnland was instructed to fabricate five carbines with a dovetail sight base on the receiver, suitable for installation of theT21 Sight. The sight itself is similar to the ramp-type sight on the M1903A3 Rifle in that it has a sliding aperture on a movable ramp base, and the ramp base moves laterally by means of a windage knob. Tests by Aberdeen Proving Ground, the Infantry Board, the Cavalry Board and the Field Artillery Board indicated that an improvement would result by modifying the adjustable sight to provide a positive method of attaching the windage knob to the windage screw. It was further recommended that range markings of 100, 150, 200, and 300 yards be properly located and placed on the sight.

USAMHI

"After waiting for days at their Elbe River bridgehead, infantrymen of the 83d Division, U.S. Ninth Army, prepare to attack the German town of Zerbat." 4/28/1945.

On left is Harold O'Donnell, of Woburn, Mass., who shoulders an M1 Carbine with a M1A2 adjustable rear sight. In center is Pfc. Morris E. Russell of Pittsburg, Texas, and on right is Pfc. William H. Holmes, 9th Army Medical Detachment, from Montgomery, West Virginia.

Photo by Tec 4 J. E. Freeney.

**U. S. Carbine, Calibre .30, M1, with M1A2
Adjustable Rear Sight Mounted—Side View**

USAMHI

November 13, 1943 — Newbury, Berkshire, England. Paratroopers of the 101st Airborne Division have just assembled their parachuted 75mm howitzer. The soldier second from left is carrying a M1A1 carbine with the stock folded. Soldier to left still has his carbine in the jump scabbard.

U.S. CARBINE, CALIBER .30, M1A1

**U.S. Carbine Caliber .30, M1A1
Stock Folded with sling**

Requirements to provide certain types of airborne troops with a short readily usable carbine caused a project to be initiated in the early part of 1942 to develop a folding stock for the carbine. Springfield Armory, Winchester Repeating Arms Company, and Inland Manufacturing Division of General Motors Corporation coordinated on this project. In March 1942, Inland submitted a side-type folding stock carbine. Infantry Board tests of this item indicated that with minor corrections it was satisfactory for infantry and parachute troops. The folding stock carbine was standardized in May 1942 and designated Carbine, Caliber .30, M1A1.

USAMHI

"82nd Airborne Division preparing to load 75 mm howitzer into glider during invasion training"
near Oujda, French Morocco in North Africa on June 11, 1943.
The center soldier from Battery A, 320th Field Artillery Battalion is carrying an M1A1 carbine.

U. S. Carbine, Caliber .30, M1A1
with stock extended and M8 Grenade Launcher

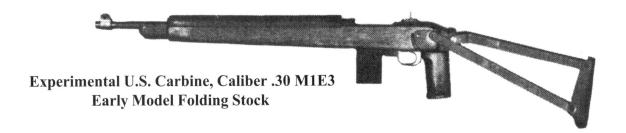

**Experimental U.S. Carbine, Caliber .30 M1E3
Early Model Folding Stock**

U.S. CARBINE, CALIBER .30, M1A3

The adoption in March 1943, of the M8 Grenade Launcher, described under the chapter heading "Grenade Launching Device for Rifles, Grenade Launcher Sights, and Pyrotechnic Projectors," reinstated further development of a folding stock carbine superior to the M1A1 Carbine, in order to permit the launching of grenades from a folding stock carbine with the stock in the open position.

Originally the Murray Corporation of America developed a stamped type of folding stock carbine. Stock, Folding, M1E3, which after several modifications and tests resulted in a design, utilizing a pantograph type stock made of solid round rod and a stock lock similar to that of the M3 Submachine Gun. A second stock, sliding type, and practically identical to that of the M3 Submachine Gun, was developed (M1E4).

Tests of the various types of stocks indicated that it was practically impossible to obtain a lightweight sliding or folding stock that would withstand the shock of launching an indefinite number of grenades (in tests the M1A1 stock broke after launching one grenade). As a result of these findings the following requirements for a folding or sliding stock were set up:

a. Must withstand the launching of 5 grenades without any tendency toward bending, cracking or weakening.

b. Must withstand the shock of firing 20 grenades before complete breakage takes place.

A series of models of improved M1E3 and M1E4 Stocks were developed and tested, finally resulting in an M1E3 Stock of such design of pantograph rods as to withstand the shock of launching 20 M11A2 Practice Grenades fired from the shoulder and stock in open position, and 20 Mk. II Fragmentation Practice Grenades with M1 Projection Adapter launched with the stock folded and the butt end of the stock on ground of various hardness. This stock was also found to be much more adaptable to firing ball ammunition than was the stock of the M1A1. As a result of the satisfactory performance of the M1E3 Carbine in tests by Aberdeen Proving Ground, the Infantry Board, and the Airborne Board, the M1E3 Carbine with a leather covering over the upper left

82nd Airborne Division, 508th Parachute Infantry Regiment soldiers wait in battle assembly area in Belgium, 6 January 1945. The soldier with the pipe in the foreground is carrying a M1A1 carbine with stock extended. The rest of the arms that can be viewed are M1 rifles.

U. S. Carbine, Caliber .30.
M1E3 Improved
Stock Folded

U. S. Carbine, Caliber .30.
M1E3 Improved
Stock Extended

U. S. Carbine, Caliber .30.
M1E4
Stock Folded

U. S. Carbine, Caliber .30.
M1E4
Stock Extended

Experimental Folding Stocks For U. S. Carbine, Caliber .30, M1

rod to protect the hirer's face in cold weather and the rear of the pistol grip slightly reshaped, was standardized in December 1943 as Carbine, Caliber .30, M1A3. The M1A1 Carbine then became Limited Standard. By the time that complete manufacturing drawings of the M1A3 were available, the status of the production of the Carbine, Caliber .30, M1A1, was such that practically the entire requirements for the years 1944 and 1945 were fulfilled. Subsequent additional quantities of folding stock carbines required were of such small numbers that establishment of manufacturing facilities and tooling to produce the M1A3 Carbine was not warranted.

U.S. CARBINE, CALIBER .30, M1E5

During the year 1942, there was an intensive demand on forging and machine tool facilities for the production of war materiel. It was therefore deemed advisable to investigate the possibilities of the use of Arma Steel for castings for the components of small arms, thus relieving the heavy demand on forging and machine tool facilities. Arma Steel was then used for trigger housings, in the later part of 1942, at the direction of Lt. General L.H. Campbell, Jr. (then Ma-

jor General), use of Arma Steel Grade "A," for carbine components was investigated. Arma Steel castings for the major components of the carbine were supplied to the Inland Manufacturing Division of General Motors Corporation by the Saginaw Division. Inland was requested to fabricate 50 carbines with all major components, except the barrel, composed of Arma Steel. Preliminary tests at Inland would be the basis of determining which components of Arma Steel would be incorporated in the carbines to be sent to Aberdeen for the standard endurance test. Inland assembled one carbine with the following components of Arma Steel: Receiver, trigger housing, hammer, recoil plate, trigger, front sight, rear sight leaf and base, bolt, and magazine catch. All other components were of standard material. The receiver on this gun was found to be broken after firing of 214 rounds. Further examination showed slight peening at the primer seat and hammer cam of the bolt, considerable peening at the firing pin striking face and the bolt cam of the hammer. All other components were in good condition. The slide and bolt were changed to a gun with a standard receiver and the test was continued through 1,000 rounds. Examination at this point showed slightly increased peening on the bolt, but this was not causing malfunctions. Conclusions drawn from this test are as follows:

  a. Arma Steel is not satisfactory for the receiver.
  b. Bolt surfaces may be locally hardened to avoid peening, but the effect of heat treatment would have to be determined by test.
  c. Arma Steel might be used to advantage in the slide.

In May 1943, 48 Carbines, M1E5, were delivered to Aberdeen. These carbines were assembled with the following Arma Steel components; operating glide, bolt, hammer, sear, trigger, trigger housing, magazine catch, and front sight. Two of these items were selected at random land subjected to the standard 6,000-round endurance test. Headspace measurements were taken prior to firing and at intervals during the firing. The opening of the headspace was so rapid that gages were not available at the Proving Center to measure the increase. When bolts and operating slides of Arma Steel proved unsatisfactory because of increased headspace and breakages, they were replaced with standard components in order to complete the test.

Based upon results of test at Aberdeen Proving Ground, and the decision reached at a meeting held 24 June 1943, which was attended by representatives of Inland, Aberdeen Proving Ground personnel, and representatives of the Ordnance Department, it was decided that Arma Steel should not be used where it might cause weakness thus harming the weapon itself. It was further decided that no further consideration be given to any components fabricated of Arma Steel other than the trigger housing, trigger, magazine catch, and hammer; the last three components would require an Austenite treatment, and then be subjected to further test. Although the front sight fabricated of Arma Steel appeared to be satisfactory, it was decided that no further consideration should be given to the use of Arma Steel in this item, inasmuch as there were approximately 50 percent breakages in manufacture.

Retest of triggers, magazine catches, and hammers fabricated of Arma Steel with an Austenite treatment were completed at Aberdeen Proving Ground. Test results vindicated that wear in the sear notch of the hammer was excessive and caused double fires, and that magazine catches and triggers withstood

endurance tests of 6,000 rounds without showing wear to any great extent.

The Inland Manufacturing Division submitted a comparative cost analysis of triggers and magazine catches made from currently specified material and Arma Steel. This cost analysis report indicated that the total cost of material and machining of the magazine catch with Arma Steel castings was slightly greater than present methods, but that total cost of triggers was slightly reduced from present methods. However, the heat treatment of the above two components required additional equipment for processing. Based upon the results of these extensive tests, it was not deemed advisable to use Arma Steel in the fabrication of carbine components, other than the trigger housing, because the slight advantage to be gained in cost savings was offset by requirement of additional equipment and non-positive quality control.

U.S. CARBINE, CALIBER .30, M1E6

This carbine, fabricated for powder testing purposes, consisted of the standard M1 Carbine equipped with a 24-inch barrel. The M1E6 Carbine was shipped to Frankford Arsenal for use in testing powders for flash

**U.S. Carbine, Caliber .30, M1E7
Equipped With Telescopic Sight**

**(Note How Front of Receiver
Differs from Standard Receiver)**

and smoke.

U.S. CARBINE, CALIBER .30, M1E7

In June 1943, at the request of Headquarters, Army Ground Forces, a project was initiated to develop a suitable mount for the adaptation of a $2\frac{1}{2}$-power telescope to the carbine without interfering with ejection of empty cartridge cases. The M1E7 Carbine, so assembled, was submitted to test at Abup under sustained firing and the endurance test was suspended. Inland Manufacturing Division of General Motors Corporation was directed to fabricate a carbine with a brazed-on telescopic mount similar to the mount of the M1903A4 Sniper's Rifle that would overcome the weakness of the first M1E7 Carbine.

Two carbines equipped with copper brazed sight mounts were tested at Aberdeen in January 1943. These tests indicated that the mounts were satisfactory from the standpoint of mechanical stability, but that there was interference with ejection. Malfunctions occurred more frequently after the ejector spring became weakened from usage. Other models of the same basic design, but with the front portion of the mount cut away so as to be flush with the rear of the chamber, proved satisfactory, but in view of the little interest shown by the using services, the item, as a lightweight sniper's rifle, was not considered for service test. However, in the early part of 1944, the Chief of Engineers, U. S. Army, requested that a study be made to determine the most practical method of modifying the carbine receiver for adaptation to it of a special infra-red viewing device known as a "Sniperscope." This equipment was to be developed in connection with a high priority project suited to jungle operations. The development work carried out on the M1E7 Carbine proved very useful in fulfilling the Engineer Board requirement and the basic design of the M1E7 was used in the development of the T3 Carbine.

Experimental Sniperscope

Details of Mount for Viewing Device on Carbine, Caliber .30, T3 Showing Modifications to the Carbine

U.S. CARBINE, CALIBER .30, T3

In order to provide a suitable mount for the carbine to meet the requirements of the Engineer Board, the following models were developed and submitted for inspection and test:

a. Carbine with brazed-on telescope mount, base centrally located with respect to the center line of the bore and special scope rings therefore.

b. Carbine with brazed-on telescope mount, base 5/8 to the left of the center line of the bore.

c. Carbine with brazed-on telescope mount as in the final model of M1E7 Carbine, previously described.

U.S. Carbine, Caliber .30, M1E7

Equipped With Telescopic Sight (Note Low Mounting On Gun)

Based upon the results of test by the Engineer Board, the M1E7 type of carbine, with a modified fore end of stock to attach the bracket of the infra-red

U.S. Carbine, Caliber .30, T3

Production Sniperscope in Searching Position

Board, the M1E7 type of carbine, with a modified fore end of stock to attach the bracket of the infra-red light source, was approved February 1944 as a procurement type and designated as Carbine, Caliber .30, T3 "Sniperscope".

At a later date, when the Sniperscope M2 was standardized, Headquarters, Army Ground Forces recommended that the Carbine T3 be standardized for use with the M2 Sniperscope. The basic weapon was to be either an M1 Carbine, or an M2 Carbine modified to allow only semi-automatic action. Tests conducted by the Engineer Board indicated that there was no appreciable difference between effects of automatic and semi-automatic fire from the Carbine, Caliber .30, M2 (described in a later portion of this chapter) on the electrical and optical components of the Sniperscope, M2. In view of the above, the Carbine, Caliber .30, M2, modified essentially in accordance with the stock and receiver design of the Carbine, T3, complete with a T23 type Flash Hider, was adopted in August 1945, and designated as Carbine, Caliber .30, M3.

During the period of standardization of the M3 Carbine, the Engineers modified the Sniperscope, M2 to incorporate the infra-red equipment, switch and electronic tube as a unit, thus eliminating the need for a modified stock.

FLASH HIDER, M3 (T3 MODIFIED)

Late in 1944 a development was initiated wherein the Aberdeen Proving Ground was requested to establish the cone dimensions for a cone type flash hider for the Carbine, Caliber .30, M2, similar to that of the Hider, Flash, M2 for the M1C and M1D Sniper's Rifles. In this instance the angle of cone had to be decreased slightly from that of the M2 Flash Hider so it would not produce sight line interference. Based upon the established cone dimensions, a drawing was prepared by the Ordnance Department wherein a cone having an included angle of $11^{1}/_{2}$ degrees and 2-inch length, was assembled to the clamp portion of the M8 Grenade Launcher and this design was designated as Hider, Flash, T23. Six pilot models of this design were fabricated and two of them were submitted to test at the Ordnance Research Center lo determine the effectiveness in hiding flash when firing the Carbine, Caliber .30, M2, in total and semi-darkness, in both semi- and full-automatic fire, observing flash at 50, 75, and 100 yards range, at an angle of 20 degrees to the line of fire. The Research Center was further instructed to check the effect on accuracy of this type flash hider, the mechanical stability of the wing nut, and to attempt to modify the flash hider in various ways to produce a combined flash hider and anti-climb device.

In the interim a requirement was set up by the Office, Chief of Engineers for a flash hider to be used in conjunction with the T3 Carbine and M2 Sniperscope.

One model of the T23 Flash Hider was turned over to the Engineer Board for test. Based upon the satisfactoriness of this design, the Office, Chief of Engineers requested that the T23 Flash Hider be classified as limited procurement type. Under this program, 1,700 T23 Flash Hiders were procured for the Office, Chief of Engineers.

Headquarters, Army Ground Forces, transmitted Infantry Board Report of test of flash hiders (flash hider- silencers) for the Carbine, Caliber .30, M1, wherein it was recommended that the following be developed:

    a. Efficient conical hider with suitable and satisfactory fastening device.

    b. An adequate recoil check that will satisfactorily perform the functioning of holding the muzzle in a horizontal plane when the carbine is fired full automatically.

    c. Combination flash hider and recoil check in one instrument that will furnish the desired results mentioned in a., and b., above.

The Ordnance Research Center tests of the T23 Flash Hider, and various modifications to attempt to

3rd Infantry Division, landing south of Anzio, 22 January 1944. The two soldiers on the left and one at center right are armed with M1 carbines — the remainder are armed with Model 1903 rifles.

percent effective in hiding flash; that the wing nut tended to loosen after approximately 75 rounds of fire; that the accuracy of the carbine was not appreciably affected by the attachment of the flash hider. It was determined that all attempts to produce a combined flash hider and anti-climb device were not successful because as the function of anti-climb was improved, the function of flash-hiding quality was decreased. The various modifications made to arrive at a satisfactory solution of the problem included cutting back the cone at various angles, extending the

maximum diameter of the cone and cutting it at various angles, and other means of introducing downward gas impingement area.

For investigating the possibilities of a better means of attaching the flash hider to the carbine, models T23E1 and T23E2 were developed. These models utilized a bayonet type lock, but proved unsatisfactory due to the accumulated tolerances in front sight diameter and the location of the rear of the front sight with respect to muzzle of barrel. They were consequently dropped from the program. Furthermore, to eliminate the possible interference of the wing nut in the line of sight, a modified version of the T23 Flash Hider, designated as T23Y or T23 modified, was developed. In this instance the wing nut hung below the barrel when the hider was assembled to the carbine.

In firing of various models of the T23 Flash Hider and M8 Grenade Launchers, both utilizing the same type of clamp arrangement, it was noted that the wing

Hider, Flash, M3

nut tended to loosen under sustained firing. Investigation disclosed that a wing nut having an inserted nylon molded washer offered enough resistance to loosening during sustained firing.

Headquarters, Army Ground Forces was advised that pilot models of the T23 and modified flash hider complete with wing nut having nylon washer inserted, were delivered to the Infantry Board for test on 4 April 1945. Based upon the results of Infantry Board test. Headquarters, Army Ground Forces, recommended that the modified T23 Flash Hider, having a wing nut in the downward position and utilizing a wing nut with an inserted nylon washer, be adopted for use with the Carbine, Caliber .30, M2, and that the basis of issue of this flash hider be one per Carbine, Caliber .30, T3 which is a part of the Sniperscope, M2, and one each to combat and combat support troops armed with the M2 Carbine.

The Hider, Flash, M3 (T23 Modified) was recommended for standardization in August 1945, too late for production and issue in World War II.

MINOR CARBINE DESIGN CHANGES

By the later part of 1943, a good many carbines were in the hands of troops. Reports from training centers, combat theaters, and testing centers indicated breakages of operating slides, bolts, and bolt components. At various stages in the production of the carbine, dimensional changes and other slight changes were made to overcome such deficiencies as well as to minimize the number of malfunctions; however, such changes as were made, did not interfere with interchangeability. Among these changes were the round bolt with a greater cam ring on the rear, a heavier section, in the operating rod, an improved front band (wider and better retention on the stock with allowance for flotation of the barrel), slightly heavier sections in the stock at the receiver cut-out, redesigned recoil plate to allow a slight spring action, a stamped-brazed front sight to simplify production, an angular change on the handle to permit better angular cartridge ejection, a stamped-brazed

Naval Historical Center
Photo by T/S Joseph A. Bowen

"Crossing the Rhine 1945. Soldiers of the U.S. Army, 7th Infantry Regiment, 3rd Division leave the assault boat that took them across the Rhine River, 26 March 1945. They climb the enemy held east bank, next to a destroyed bridge in the Frankenthal area." Most carry M1 Carbines.

USAMHI

2nd Division, 9th Regiment Infantrymen crouch in a ditch seeking shelter from a German artillery barrage Krinkalter Woods, Germany, 14 December 1944. Note M1 carbine ready for use.

trigger housing to simplify machine operations, and a change in cam cut on the operating slide to increase the dwell time.

A series of carbines equipped with barrels having oversize land and groove dimensions were fabricated and tested in, June 1943. Results of extensive tests indicated that an increase in manufacturing tolerances from 0.001 inch to 0.002 inch in both land and groove dimensions would not affect the accuracy, velocity, or erosion of the barrel. The incorporation of these increased tolerances in carbine barrel manufacture helped speed the delivery of carbines to our troops.

U.S. CARBINE, CALIBER .30, T2

At this time it became apparent that a new type of gas system similar to that of the M1E9 Caliber .30 Rifle already described, might have some advantages to offer from the standpoint of life of components, if the dwell time of the slide could be increased and the velocity of the slide decreased at the time of contact

USAMHI

"Herman Goering's bed in the lodge he owned at Neuhaus, Germany, provides a comfortable resting place for an Infantryman of the U.S. Third Army. 4/21/45". This 71st Division GI has an M1 Carbine with a two magazine pouch around its buttstock.

"April 22, 1944. Units of the 163rd Inf., 41st Div. task force wade into shore from LST during the invasion of Aitape, New Guinea. Photo by Lt. Joseph Pinto". The three lead soldiers on left carry M1 carbines.

with the bolt during the recoil stroke, the impact against the bolt lug would be decreased and, in the over-all picture, the life of components increased.

Springfield Armory was requested to modify two carbines, using a combination of the gas expansion principle with the impulse type of recoil action. In the design of the T2 Carbine, the gas expansion operates only over 1 3/8 inches of the stroke. The remaining movement of the slide and bolt is due to the inertia acquired from the initial impulse of the gas expansion. Tests of a preliminary model showed that the dwell time was increased to three times that of the standard carbine while the residual pressure was dropped to an extremely low point. The modification required a new gas cylinder and operating slide.

A second model, designated Carbine, Caliber .30, T2E1 incorporating a gas cut-off and expansion system was fabricated and tested at Springfield Armory. Fifteen hundred rounds were fired without cleaning or lubrication and after remaining in this condition over a week-end, 500 additional rounds were fired without malfunction.

A third model designated T2E2 utilizing a modified gas impulse system was also developed. Two of each type were tested at the Ordnance Research

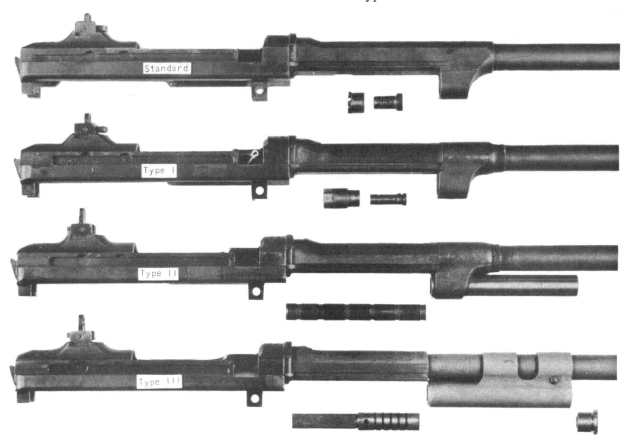

U.S. Carbine, Caliber .30, M1 with Modified Gas Systems

Center, the T2 having a built-in gas expansion system, the T2E1 having modified components to effect the gas expansion principle and the T2E2 employing the long tappet type. The guns were tested relative to instrumental velocity, accuracy, grenade firing, elevation and depression firing, endurance firing, flash and effects of mud and rain. The instrumental velocities of the three types were slightly higher than the check velocity. In the rain test, the T2 model was somewhat better than the other two experimental models and better than the standard carbine. In all other phases of the test, the experimental models were either comparable or inferior to the standard carbine.

The over-all results of the test indicated that the gas expansion system, when fully developed, would offer some improvements over the tappet system. The magnitude of these improvements, however, did not appear to be sufficient for the adaptation of the gas cylinder system to the carbine, but like the M1E9 Rifle, it offered promise in future developments.

U.S. CARBINE, CALIBER .30, M2

As the pace of the war accelerated and our troops encountered new types of terrain and new enemy tactics, the need for more fire power was anticipated. In May 1944, a research and development project was initiated to provide a group of components assembled to the standard carbine to permit semi- and full-automatic fire by means of a change lever. To obtain selected full-automatic fire on the carbine it was necessary to modify the sear, the hammer, the operating slide, and the trigger housing, and to remove a small amount of wood from the stock; this subsequently necessitated strengthening of the stock. The modification of the sear incorporated a built-up portion on the nose to permit operation of the sear release. The modification of the hammer is such as to permit cam operation of a sear trip during the free forward movement of the operating slide. The trigger housing retaining pin is modified to effect a crank action to permit selective fire. The trigger housing has a small notch to retain the change lever spring and a cut-out for the actuating lever.

The additional components are; change lever and spring, sear trip, spring and plunger, and an actuating lever. The carbine is set for full-automatic fire by moving the change lever located on the left side of the receiver forward. When the trigger is held back, as the slide goes forward at the last portion of its for-

SELECTOR SHOWN IN SEMI-AUTOMATIC POSITION

NEW CURVED 30 ROUND MAGAZINE

U.S. Carbine, Caliber .30, M2 (T4)
Left Side View

ward movement, the cam cut on the right side of the slide cams the front end of the actuating lever downward. This in turn forces the rear end of the lever upward, thus forcing the front end of the sear release upward. This action forces the rear end of the sear release downward against the lug on the sear which forces the sear out of the sear notch on the hammer and permits the hammer to fall. The new trigger housing retaining pin (actuating lever crank pin) on which the actuating lever is pivoted is eccentric relative to the body of the pin, thus permitting the change lever, when moved, to locate the actuating lever in either the position for camming action or noncamming action during movement of the operating slide. During semi-automatic firing, normal operation of the various components takes place.

The additional and modified components were designated as Kit, Carbine, T17. The carbine assembled with these components, developed by Inland in accordance with basic design suggested by this office, was designated, Carbine, Caliber .30, T4.

The design of selective semi- and full-automatic fire as developed by Springfield Armory, and designated T18, operated by means of the hammer delay through a mechanical disadvantage incurred through a hammer delay mechanism. Due to the variations in spring tension, friction and weight of components, this design of mechanism would not permit uniform functioning from carbine to carbine and therefore was given no further consideration.

In conjunction with the development of the automatic carbine, a development of a 30-round capacity magazine was initiated. Exploratory work in connection with the 30-round magazine indicated the necessity for a new magazine catch to permit greater area of support. This was necessary due to the added weight acting on the magazine nibs, thus causing them to batter and shear off with but very slight usage. In

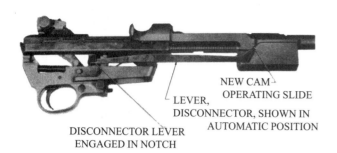

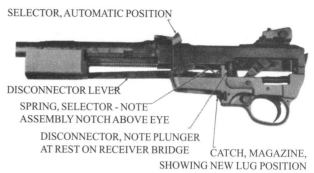

**U.S. Carbine, Caliber .30, M2 (T4)
Mechanism, Right Side View**

**U.S. Carbine, Caliber .30, M2 (T4)
Mechanism, Left Side View**

the modified magazine catch the left end carries an extension at right angles to the catch. This type of magazine catch permits the use of either the standard 15-round magazine or the new design of 30-round magazine and is interchangeable with existing magazine catches. Magazines having two nibs, as on the present standard magazine, plus an additional nib to act as an auxiliary magazine catch support, would have sufficient area to eliminate the above described deficiency. Both 30- and 15-round magazines may thus be used interchangeably in the standard carbine and the carbine equipped with full-automatic.

The initial model of T4 Carbine was submitted to the Infantry Board for test. Test results indicated that the item was satisfactory for infantry use. The Infantry Board stated that short bursts in full-automatic fire are not to be visualized as the customary way of using an automatic carbine even though the selective automatic mechanism was incorporated in its construction. The short burst and full-automatic availability, while successful, is a fire capability for use in an emergency and not as habitual technique.

Twelve additional T4 Carbines were fabricated for engineering test: Four T4 Carbines were tested at the Ordnance Research Center during September 1944, with the following results:

a. Preliminary function fire of 100 rounds satisfactory.

b. Elevation and depression firing:
Two failures to feed due to override, and one failure to feed when the round cocked entering the chamber.

c. Cyclic rate of fire; 750-775 rounds per minute.

d. Accuracy: At 100 yards, muzzle and elbow rest, semi-automatic fire, there was no significant difference in accuracy during any phase of the test. At 50 yards, full-automatic fire, using a 6x6 foot target, fired in 5-round bursts, using gunners of various degrees of skill, the firer's proficiency increased from an average of 50 percent hits to 85 percent hits.

e. In the endurance firing of 6,000 rounds per gun, the number of malfunctions and breakages was comparable to the standard M1 Carbine.

f. Weight:
Standard Carbine — 5 pounds, 1.85 ounces
T4 Carbine — 5 pounds, 3.19 ounces

In September 1944, the Carbine, Caliber .30, T4 was approved as a Service Test Type and the contract for 500 carbines and 8,500 thirty-round capacity magazines plus the necessary spare parts for maintenance was initiated. In view of the fact that the 30-round magazines were not available upon completion of the 500 Carbines, T4, the carbines were shipped to Service Boards and combat theaters with the standard 15-round capacity magazines having flame hardened nibs.

During the period that these 500 carbines were being made, the Infantry Board at Fort Benning, Georgia; the Aberdeen Proving Ground; the Tank Destroyers at Camp Hood, Texas, the Cavalry Board at Fort Riley, Kansas; the Marine Corps Equipment Board at Quantico, Virginia had run extended engineering and tactical tests which resulted in their all recommending that this new carbine should replace the M1. The M2 Carbine, as it is now called, was

**New Magazine Catch and 30-Round
Magazine for Carbine, Caliber .30, M2**

magazines having the above described follower were procured and designated as Magazine, Carbine, T18. One hundred and fifty of these were shipped to the Infantry Board for test, and based upon the results of this test, the 30-round capacity magazine equipped with the T18 type follower was adopted for use with the carbines, caliber .30, in April 1945, and designated as Magazine Assembly (30-round) Drawing No. 7162176.

made a standard weapon in September 1944, and the M1 and M1A1 and M1A3 Carbines were reclassified as Limited Standard.

The 8,500 magazines were completed during the early part of April 1945 and in accordance with the request of Headquarters, Army Ground Forces, magazines were shipped to the following service boards for informative purposes: Infantry Board, Fort Benning, Georgia; Field Artillery Board, Fort Bragg, N. Carolina, Cavalry Board, Fort Riley, Kansas, Armored Board, Fort Knox, Kentucky; and the Airborne Center, Fort Sill, Oklahoma.

Tests of these items at the manufacturing facility and informal tests witnessed by representatives of Headquarters, Army Ground Forces, indicated that the subject items were satisfactory for use with the carbines, caliber .30.

In October and November 1942, during the test of experimental carbines, magazines having a follower modified to retain the bolt in the open position after the last round had been fired were tested at Aberdeen Proving Ground. This was a test of experimental carbines rather than of magazines; however, the test indicated that magazines with this type follower performed the usual magazine functions equally as well as the standard item, and in addition would retain the bolt in the open position after firing the last round. Further tests showed no damage to the bolt face, the magazine catch, or the follower. However, the results were inconclusive in that the test was too brief, and there were not enough carbines with this type of magazine tested.

In October 1944, approval was granted for the development of a carbine magazine follower with nib modified to retain the bolt in the open position after the last round had been fired. Two hundred and fifty

STANDARD MAGAZINE	MAGAZINE, T18
A1 - MAGAZINE CASE	A2 - MAGAZINE CASE
B1 - FOLLOWER SPRING	B2 - FOLLOWER SPRING
C1 - MAGAZINE BASE PLATE	C2 - MAGAZINE BASE PLATE
D1 - MAGAZINE FOLLOWER (NOTE TAPERED FOLLOWER LIP)	D2 - MAGAZINE FOLLOWER (ARROW DENOTES CRIMPED LIP OF HOLD-BACK FEATURE)

**Component Parts of
Standard 15-round Carbine
Magazine as compared
with the Magazine, T18**

(ALL PARTS OF THE. TWO MAGAZINES
ARE IDENTICAL WITH THE EXCEPTION OF THE
FOLLOWER LIP MARKED BY ARROWS 1 AND 2)

NEW SAFETY FOR CARBINE

Reports were received from the field to the effect that the location of the carbine safety being just to the rear of the magazine catch results in considerable and serious difficulty because the user inadvertently releases the magazine when attempting to push the safety to "fire" position. The feel of the magazine catch which projects to the same horizontal level as the safety when in the "safe" position is so similar that men with cold hands or under other difficulties in combat, such as wet and darkness, cannot readily distinguish between the carbine safety catch and the magazine catch.

Recognizing the desirability of eliminating the possible confusion of the safety with the magazine catch, Springfield Armory was instructed to fabricate two sample types of improved carbine safeties, namely, Tl and T2. Both safeties are lever operated, rotational types, which replace the present safety without any modification to the trigger housing. The Tl Safety, mounted on the right side of the carbine, when in the "safe off" position, has the lever to the rear and is rotated approximately 90 degrees counter clockwise to the "safe on" position. The T2 Safety, mounted on the left side of the carbine, when in the "safe off" position, has the lever facing forward and is rotated approximately 90 degrees counterclockwise to the "safe on" position. The T3 Safety, a sliding type, was found upon inspection to be unsatisfactory and consequently no further consideration was given to this item.

The deficiency pertaining to the existing safety was confirmed in a paraphrase of a message from the European Theater of Operations. Samples of the T1 and T2 Safeties were tested by the Infantry Board, Cavalry Board and Marine Corps Equipment Board, and resulted in a decision to adopt the Tl. The Safety, Carbine, Ordnance Drawing No. 7162080 (Tl) was adopted in March 1945 for inclusion as a standard component in all carbines of future manufacture and for replacement of the present safety in all carbines in use.

MISCELLANEOUS ITEMS PERTAINING TO THE CARBINE

PLASTIC CARBINE STOCK

When the Cartridge, Grenade, Auxiliary, M7 was standardized it was recommended that appropriate training manuals, in particular those relating to the carbine, be revised to show the purpose of limitation of the auxiliary grenade cartridge. The carbine is not structurally designed to maintain serviceability when firing this cartridge.

It appeared desirable to investigate the possibility of developing a plastic stock for the carbine which is stronger and more durable than the present wood stock. Inland Manufacturing Division of General Motors Corporation developed and fabricated samples of the T7 Stock utilizing a Bakelite material impregnated with canvas fibers and finished with an olive-drab "flock" covering. Various tests as to usability, shock, and cold tests indicated satisfactory performance, but under actual conditions of launching grenades using the auxiliary cartridge, breakages in the section behind the recoil plate and at the "neck" of the pistol grip resulted. Further investigation into plastic materials and processing resulted in the T7E1 Stock. Factory tests of this item indicated nonuniformity in strength from stock to stock.

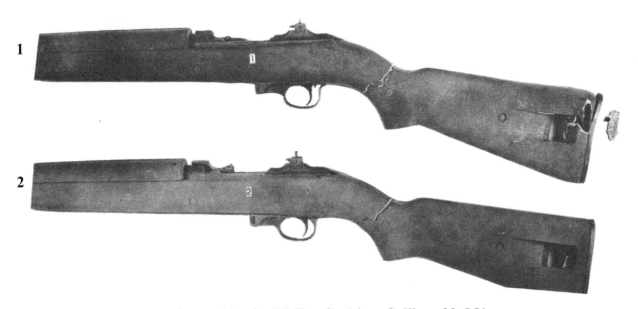

Stock, Plastic, T7 For Carbine, Caliber .30, M1

No. 1: Condition after 8th Round
No. 2: Condition after 6th Round

The primary difficulty to date in producing satisfactory plastic stocks is the inability to control uniform location of the fibers in the plastic material when the material is subjected to pressure during molding, consequently, development was discontinued.

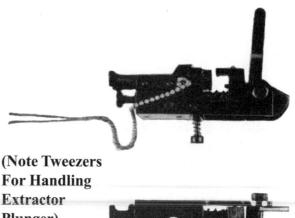

(Note Tweezers For Handling Extractor Plunger)

Front band bayonet lug assembly

Close-up of front band bayonet lug assembly

Tool, Carbine Bolt, T4E1 Carbine Bolt in Place Ready For Disassembly

CARBINE BOLT TOOLS

The T4E1 Carbine bolt disassembly and assembly tool, developed from its predecessor, the T4, is of such, design as to permit its use as a 4th Echelon tool. It may be clamped in a vise or permanently fastened to a bench and utilizes a spring-loaded cam to depress the ejector spring, a finger to depress the extractor plunger and; spring, plus a spring-loaded extractor remover usable while the bolt assembly is held by means of two projecting lips over the locking lugs. One hundred of these items were completed and turned over to the Field Service, Maintenance Division, in December 1944 for distribution to ordnance installations.

FRONT BAND BAYONET LUG ASSEMBLY FOR CARBINE.

The Front Band Bayonet Lug Assembly, T2, was developed to permit the use of the M4 Bayonet Knife as a bayonet for the carbine. This design incorporated the new design of front band assembly previously described plus an extension thereto, which carried a bayonet lug. This item, designated as Band, Upper, Assembly, Drawing No. C71600963, was adopted in May 1944 to replace previous designs of front band assemblies in manufacture and in the field.

Carbine, Caliber .30, M1 made by National Postal Meter with New Front Band Assembly and M1A2 Adjustable Rear Sight. A survey of Army Signal Corps photos indicates that few of these arms saw service in World War II. Their call to service would come in the Korean War five years later.

Based upon the request of Field Service, a project was initiated in December 1944 to develop a carbine bolt disassembly tool for Second Echelon use. This tool was designated as Tool, Bolt, Carbine, T5. In this design the bolt is laid into a short half circular base section.

Through the rotation of a screw the bolt is moved forward so that a pin in the head of the base section depresses the ejector and the extractor release depresses the extractor plunger. This allows the extractor to be removed and the balance of the carbine bolt disassembled. Assembly of the bolt is handled in the reverse manner with the exception that the extractor release component is rotated 180 degrees in order to permit the assembly claw to positively locate the flat of the extractor plunger, in the proper position during assembly of the bolt

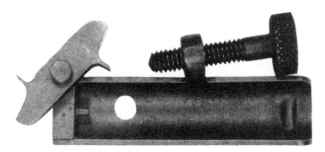

Carbine Bolt Tool T5

Springfield Armory was requested to fabricate two pilot models in accordance with a design submitted. Upon completion of the two pilot models, and approval of Field Service, a Research and Development Contract was placed for the fabrication of 100 pilot model carbine bolt tools made in accordance with the Springfield Armory drawings. These items were turned over to Field Service, Maintenance Division, of the Ordnance Department in June 1945 as a completed development.

RECOIL CHECK

Based upon results of service tests and tests in theaters of combat of the preproduction model Carbine, Caliber .30, M2, Headquarters, Army Ground Forces, requested that a project be initiated to develop an adequate recoil check that would satisfactorily perform the function of holding the muzzle in a horizontal plane when the carbine is fired automatically.

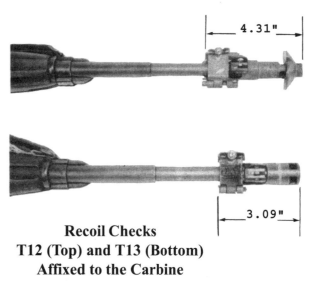

**Recoil Checks
T12 (Top) and T13 (Bottom)
Affixed to the Carbine**

Springfield Armory was requested to fabricate six recoil checks for the carbine to be made in accordance with an exploratory model developed at the Armory, and similar to that used on the T20E1 Rifle. One model recoil check, designated as T12, was completed and informally submitted to the Infantry Board, through Headquarters, Army Ground Forces, for test.

A limited amount of firing indicated that the recoil dampening effect on the carbine could be minimized and emphasis placed upon the muzzle depression effect, thus decreasing the over-all size of the recoil check. In view of this, further development was initiated to produce a device to give the required end results. Six sample recoil checks made in accordance with Ordnance Department design and designated as Check, Recoil, T13, were fabricated. The T13 Recoil Check differs from the T12 in that consideration has been given to offset of climb rather than to minimization of recoil.

Based upon results of Infantry Board tests, the T13 Recoil Check modified with wing nut in downward position, was recommended for adoption in September 1945.

CARBINE CARTRIDGE CLIP

With the adoption of the M2 Carbine and the 30-round magazine, it became evident that the greater fire power and magazine capacity provided would necessitate the use of greater quantities of ammunition. To facilitate ease of loading the larger capacity magazine some study was given to the possibility of making a clip for the carbine cartridge similar to that

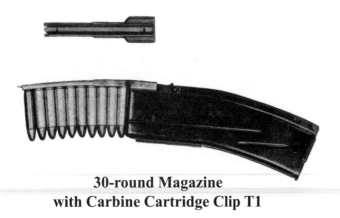

**30-round Magazine
with Carbine Cartridge Clip T1**

of the M1903 Rifle, and it was concluded that such a cartridge clip could be developed to have characteristics as follows:

a. A 10-round cartridge capacity.

b. Incorporate a member to permit convenient and rapid loading of cartridges into the carbine magazine.

c. Pack readily into standard type bandoleers, which will hold 18 to 24 ten-round clips.

d. Filled bandoleer would pack into the standard Can, Ammunition, Packing Carbine, M6, and thereby provide waterproof packaging without development of a special container.

e. Be of such simplicity of design as to be capable of mass production.

A prototype physical sample of a cartridge clip with the above characteristics has been fabricated and inspected in the Office, Chief of Ordnance. It is expected that with minor modification it will satisfactorily fulfill the requirement; thereby a satisfactory design can be achieved without delay. This sample, properly modified, has been designated Clip, Cartridge, Carbine (10-round), Tl.

BLANK FIRING ATTACHMENT FOR THE CARBINE.

The Director of Military Training invited attention to the following facts:

a. Eighty-five percent of personnel assigned to Army Service Forces T/O Units are armed with the carbine.

b. Revision of Mobilization Training Programs of Army Service Forces units stresses field exercises in the preparation of units for operation against the Japanese.

c. Reports from the Pacific and Asiatic Theaters indicate that service type units must be well qualified to defend the area, which they are occupying, against infiltration, raids, and the various ruses employed by the Japanese.

d. Many of these service type units are left to themselves on the small scattered islands throughout the Pacific where bases are located.

In view of these considerations, a project for a blank firing attachment was initiated in June 1945. The T12 Blank Firing Attachment currently under development utilizes the clamp arrangement of the M8 Grenade Launcher with the tube cut off just forward of the muzzle counterbore and cupped over with a ported cap having a port of such size as to permit the carbine to be fired either semi- or full-automatic when using blank cartridges.

DUST CAPS FOR CARBINE MAGAZINE

In order to eliminate the possibility of feed failures in the carbine due to dirt accumulation in loaded magazines a plastic Dust Cap T3, was developed in June 1945 and submitted to the service boards for test. Its design permits ready removal from the magazine by striking the protruding nibs against any sharp portion of the carbine.

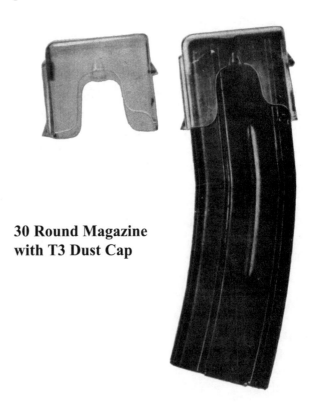

**30 Round Magazine
with T3 Dust Cap**

Troops of 24th Division, 21st Infantry Regiment disembark from troopship into landing craft, 3rd wave, for invasion of Leyete, Philippine Islands, 20 October 1944. Photo by Pvt. Archie Stone. The soldier in foreground has a M1 carbine slung over his arm.

The original caption reads only "92nd Div Troops, 1945?" The scene appears to be in Italy, with the two GIs on left carrying M1 carbines. The officer, fourth from left, has drawn his .45 automatic, and the GI in the right foreground is carrying a M1903A3 bolt action rifle.

Omaha Beach — D-Day plus one

2nd Infantry Division infantrymen — the lead three are carrying Model 1903 rifles. The original caption reads: "Allied Reinforcements arrive in Normandy. U.S. troops move up in an endless stream from a beach in Normandy to reinforce Allied Soldiers fighting in Northern France. Motorized equipment fills the parking area as supplies flow across the English Channel night and day." The 2nd Infantry Division arrived at Normandy's Omaha Beach on D-Day plus one.

Model 1917 .30 Caliber Rifle — The Enfield

The Model 1917 .30 Caliber rifle, known as the Enfield, resulted from a World War I British Purchasing Commission contracting with the arms-making firms of Winchester and Remington (at Ilion and Eddystone) to make .303 Caliber rifles based on their 1914 Pattern. Upon the entry of the U.S into the 1st World War a decision was made to convert the production to the standard 30-06 U.S. government cartridge to meet US mobilization needs. This decision would be repeated in 1941 with the Model 1903 machinery at Remington. The M1917 rifles still in inventory would be issued for guard and training use and sent to our Allies.

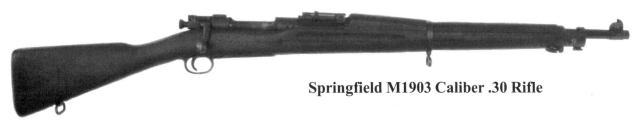

Springfield M1903 Caliber .30 Rifle

THE 1903 SPRINGFIELD

PRODUCTION BY REMINGTON

The end of World War I brought the cessation of Model 1903 Rifle production at the Rock Island Arsenal. By June 1919, with 317,000 rifles having been produced in its two years of operation, the decision was made to stop production and place into storage the Rock Island machinery for manufacturing the Model 1903 Rifle. Likewise, with the development of the Garand M1 rifle in the 1930's the decision was made to replace the old overhead belt driven machinery at Springfield Armory with new machinery along with new buildings. By 1940 all the Springfield 1903 rifle machinery was shipped to Rock Island Arsenal for storage. The British Purchasing Commission had approached the Remington Arms Company with a contract to produce a half million rifles – but the company had insufficient capacity. The U.S. Ordnance Department suggested the use of the 1903 Rifle machinery stored at Rock Island, Illinois. An agreement was made and the machinery was shipped to the Remington plant in Ilion, New York. The 1903 rifle machinery, as earlier noted, utilized overhead shafting and leather belting for power, with which, fortunately, the Remington plant in Ilion was already equipped.

However, the Ordnance Department soon realized that shipments of M1917 and M1903 rifles under Lend Lease agreements to Britain had severely de-pleted the United States store of arms and advised Remington the machinery would be best used to produce M1903 rifles for the United States in the 30-06 caliber, versus a redesigned .303 caliber rifle for the British. A cost plus fixed fee contract was signed with Remington Arms Company in March 1941. The British need for a million rifles would be met by the Savage-Stevens Company of Chicopee Falls, Massachusetts, who would produce over a million Short Lee Enfields during the war for our British allies – these rifles being provided under the Lend Lease agreements were marked "U.S. Property", with only the letter "S" marked on them to signify the manufacturing firm of Savage-Stevens.

The first production of the 1903 rifle by Remington was in November 1941, aided by the excellent storage methods employed two decades previously at Rock Island, which included the necessary gauges, tools, and cutters. In March 1942 another contract was let for 1903 rifles with the L.C. Smith & Corona Typewriters, Inc. of Syracuse, New York – for this contract new machinery would be procured. Meanwhile at Ilion 100,000 1903 Rifles were delivered by Remington by the end of May 1942. In December 1942 with 350,000 rifles already produced, a less costly, and more effective stamped rear sight mounted on the rear of the receiver versus on the barrel was

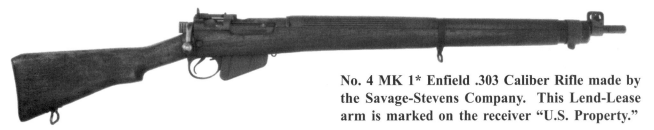

No. 4 MK 1* Enfield .303 Caliber Rifle made by the Savage-Stevens Company. This Lend-Lease arm is marked on the receiver "U.S. Property."

Our British Allies allowed the use of the M1903 Rifle machinery at Remington to produce .30 Caliber M1903 rifles for the U.S. They turned to the firm of Savage-Stevens of Chicopee Falls, Massachusetts who produced over a million .303 caliber No. 4 MK 1* Enfield Rifles during World War II. A portion of these arms were made at the old Massachusetts Arms Company's Lamb Knitting building, which had made Smith and Maynard carbines during the Civil War.

Springfield M1903 with milled trigger guard, floor plate and bands

Springfield M1903A1 with a "C" stock having a full pistol grip refurbished in World War II with a two-groove barrel.

USAMHI

"Bantam car which was rammed by a 2 1/2 ton truck". This 1st Infantry Division Willeys Jeep was equipped with a rifle scabbard holding a Model 1903 rifle.

brought into production – this change would cause the Rifle to be redesignated as Model 1903A3 – 700,000 03-A3's were to be produced during the remaining year of production. Direction was given in November 1943 to cease production of complete rifles at both plants by 29 February 1944. Approximately a million 1903 and 1903A3 rifles were produced by Remington during the war.

While in production there were constant requests for changes to simplify manufacture – the primary ones were the replacement of forged and milled parts with parts produced by stamping – the butt plate, trigger guard, magazine floor plate, front and rear bands

being amongst the changes – all resulting in savings with the new stamped parts averaging one tenth the cost of the milled parts. There was also a partial attempt to produce the Model 1903A1 stock with a pistol grip – however the stock blanks ordered would not allow a full pistol grip – thus a partial or "scant" stock was authorized in May 1942.

TWO-GROOVED RIFLING

In an effort to speed up production of caliber .30 rifle barrels, early in 1942 it was proposed to reduce the number of grooves from four to two. To determine the effect of reducing the number of grooves, comparative tests of two- and four-groove rifle barrels were conducted at Aberdeen Proving Ground. As a control, four M1903A3 Rifles with two grooves and standard bore dimensions were tested. All two-groove barrels tested had groove dimensions identical to those of the four-groove barrels; that is, the two-groove barrels were fabricated by merely omitting one pair of grooves without making any change in the width or depth of the remaining two grooves. Aberdeen Proving Ground test results indicated that the performance of the two-groove barrel was in every way equal to that of the standard four-groove barrel. Accordingly, Ordnance Committee action (OCM 19053-22 October 1942) was taken recommending adoption of two-groove rifling for use in U.S. Rifles, Caliber .30, M1903A1, M1903A3, M1917, and M1. Barrels having two-groove rifling were produced for the M1903 and M1917 Rifles, but there were never any made for the M1 Rifle. Subsequently, this design was deleted from M1 Rifle drawings.

USAMHI

12-29-1942
North Africa

Above — P-38 Fighter of the 14th Fighter Group, Youks Las Baines, is being tractored to repair area. Its engine was damaged by a German Fighter. The three soldiers at left carry M1903 Rifles. The airman in leather jacket is sitting on a Model 1928A1 Thompson Submachine Gun.

Naval Historical Center

Bluejacket practicing with M1903 Rifle.

Naval Historical Center
December, 1941

Sentry with M1903 Rifle, on flagship USS Wichita off Reykjavik, Iceland.

USAMHI

186309

Soldiers of the 148th Infantry, 37th Division climbing cargo net of the transport SS President Jackson taking them to Bougainville. 11-5-43. The bottom two infantrymen are carrying Model 1903 bolt action rifles, upper GIs Garands.

USAMHI

3rd Division, 15th Infantry landing at St. Tropez, France 15 August 1944. The soldier on the left is carrying a Model 1903 rifle fitted with an M1 grenade launcher. The amphibious tank carries the collapsible skirt, which had failed in the rougher waters off Omaha Beach on D-Day.

U.S. RIFLE CALIBER .30, M1903A3

During the early part of 1942, it seemed desirable to redesign the rear leaf-type sight of the M1903 Rifle in order to reduce the requirements for machine tools and to bring the sight more in line with the M1 Rifle rear sight. A ramp-type sight was designed to be located on the rear bridge of the receiver. It permits elevation adjustments from 200 to 800 yards by means of a sliding peep on the ramp and right and left windage adjustment by means of a windage knob to move the ramp laterally. This sight could be manufactured for less money than its forerunner, was simpler to use, and was less difficult to service. The peep being closer to the rifleman's eye reduced the time required for alignment on the target and the longer sight radius provided for greater accuracy. The M1903 rifle equipped with the new ramp-type sight was adopted as the M1903A3 by Ordnance Committee on 21 May 1942, with production in December.

Remington M1903 with stamped sheet metal trigger guard, floor plate, and bands

M1903A3 .30 caliber rifle, with straight stock and front sight protector

Remington M1903A3 rifle with scant stock

Naval Historical Center

"**Buchenwald Concentration Camp, Germany. An emaciated prisoner, wearing the striped camp uniform pants, shows the results of the camp's starvation diet, 18 April 1945. Other prisoners are talking with U.S. Army soldiers who are touring the camp.**"

Note the Springfield M1903A3 Rifle carried by the soldier. The machinery used at Remington to produce the 1903 rifle had been earlier used to produce Springfield Model 1861 Rifle Muskets, the primary Union arm of the Civil War - the war that would end slavery in the United States. The contributing author's Uncle, Frank W. Green, witnessed the horrors of the Dachau concentration camp. His Division, the 80th Division, participated in the liberation of the Buchenwald camp.

Naval Historical Center

"Marines Boarding USS LCI-340 on the day before Christmas 1943. They landed at Cape Gloucester." The Marine at left has a M1903A4 Rifle, next a Thompson, the rest Garands.

USAMHI

82nd Airborne paratroopers inspecting an abandoned German truck in Sicily, 11 July 1943. Soldier on left is cradling a M1903A4. Note no front sight and front end of Weaver scope.

Remington M1903A4 with Weaver M73B1 2.2-Power Scope. The stock has the full "C" pistol grip, the barrel was cut for a front sight, and the bolt handle was redesigned to clear the scope.

U.S. RIFLE, CALIBER .30, M1903A4

In order to meet urgent overseas requirements for rifles equipped with telescopes for use by snipers, tests were conducted by the Infantry Board and manufacturing investigations were conducted by the Ordnance Department to alter and fit several M1903 Rifles with commercial types of telescopes.

In the latter part of 1942, Headquarters, Army Ground Forces, as a result of the above investigations, recommended that a hunting type of telescope, as exemplified by the Weaver 330-C, be mounted above the receivers of the M1903 or M1903A1 Rifles initially for immediate production; that the

"Check and Double Check" — "Private First Class, Edward J. Foley, Company "C", 143rd Infantry, 36th Division of Nethuan, Massachusetts gives his M1903A4 sniper rifle a thorough check before going up front near Velletri, Italy on 29 May 1944." The soldier on the left is holding a M1 Garand, while the rest of his squad are holding Model 1903 bolt action rifles.

rifles to be used were to be especially selected for accuracy and smoothness of operation; that the type "C" stocks with full pistol grip be used if available; and that the bolt handles be so remodeled as to eliminate interference with the sight. The M1903A4 Rifle adopted in December 1942 met the above requirements through the use of the Redfield Junior type of mount fastened to the receiver (slightly modified) of the M1903A1 Rifle, less iron sights, and utilizing either the 2°-power Weaver Telescope (designated as M73B1) or the Lyman Alaskan Telescope (designated as M73). The M73 was never put into use. A modified M1903A1 stock with pistol grip (drawing D1836) was used on this rifle. As a result of combat experience in tropical climates, the need for a telescope to be fungusproof, waterproof, and practically shockproof, was indicated. The development of a telescope to replace the commercial types of telescopes described in this chapter was undertaken by the Artillery Development Division and resulted in the standardization, early in 1945, of the Telescope M84 to replace the M73. Approximately 25,000 M1903A4 rifles were produced during the war.

USAMHI WWII Survey — Paul Kuchinos

5th Armored Division meets with Russians. The upright rifle in foreground is a M1903A4.

USAMHI

Anzio area, 26 January 1944. 82nd Infantry Division, 504th Airborne Infantry, 2nd Battalion crossing the Mussolini Canal. Paratrooper on the left shoulders a M1903A4 sniper rifle.

Soldiers of 71st Infantry Division in Canal Zone, Panama, April 14, 1942. The 1903 Rifle at left has been field modified to a shorter length to aid in jungle operations.

"1st Squad, 3rd Platoon, Co. A, 508th P.I.R., 82nd Div, June 5, 1944"

Trooper of the 82nd Airborne in North Africa displaying the new scoped M1903A4 rifle.

Note the M1903 rifle in front row center.

Stewards Mates School, 26 April 1944, N.A.S. Seattle Washington, drilling with M1903 rifles

"Armistice Day parade, Noumea, New Caledonia." The Sailors in formation carry M1903 Rifles; Petty Officers holstered .45 Automatics and the Officer a holstered revolver.

"Marine sniper using a special weapon. He is Pfc. Hiram W. Westbrook, II, 19, of San Angelo, Texas. July 2, 1944, Saipan." Photograph by Sgt. J. W. Combs. He has just fired a M1903A1 rifle mounted with an eight-power telescope made by the Unertl Optical Company. The Unertl scope has moved forward by inertia, and must be pulled rearward into firing position, as below.

United States Marine Corps altered Model 1903A1 rifle mounted with an eight-power telescope made by the Unertl Optical Company of Pittsburgh, Pennsylvania. This rifle was reissued during the Korean War where it was used by a U.S. Marine sniper who was killed in action. The rifle was sent home by fellow Marines to his family in Northern Kentucky. It was sold by his son in the mid-1950's.

USMC USE OF THE 1903 RIFLE

The M1 Garand semi-automatic rifle had been adopted by the Army in January 1936 and had reached a production rate of 1000 a day by 1941. However, the Garand versus Johnson Rifle controversy of 1940 resulted in a trial of the Johnson Semi-Automatic rifle at the Marine Base in San Diego, California in November 1940. These tests included the M1 Garand, a rifle submitted by Winchester, and a 1903 Springfield. The tests featured an endurance test of 12,000 rounds, which found the Johnson rifle subject to parts breakage substantiating the superiority of the M1. The Marine Corps did not, however, adopt the M1 semi-automatic rifle at that time, instead retaining for their use the 1903 Springfield bolt-action rifle. Though the M1 was adopted in 1941, they retained their M1903 Rifles through the early Pacific islands campaigns, with the Guadalcanal campaign being noteworthy in proving to the Marine soldier the M1's superiority in firepower as well as reliability. By 1943 the M1 had superseded the 1903 Rifle in the Marine Corps, though the 1903 Rifle continued in use in decreasing numbers by the Marine Corps throughout the war.

The Marine Corps also utilized a different scope mounted sniper rifle than the 1903A4 bolt-action rifle or the M1C semi-automatic rifle adopted by the Army. The Marine Corps utilized M1903A1 rifles mounted with eight-power telescopes made by the Unertl Optical Company of Pittsburgh, Pennsylvania. This company would also produce numerous other optical parts, including artillery sights, as part of their war production effort. Three thousand rifles are believed to have been assembled at the Marine Corps Depot in Philadelphia.

Marine Corps Historical Center

"In orderly columns, the Marines move out by sections and board the boats which will take them from Guadalcanal beach to the waiting transports." Undated. The Marines still carry their bolt-action 1903 Springfield rifles, that would be replaced with the semi-automatic M1 Garand rifle.

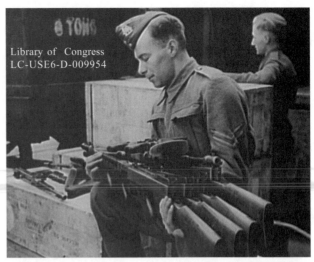

Shipment of Lend Lease M1928A1 Thompson Submachine Guns being unpacked in England.

Two men from 43rd Infantry Division, 172nd Infantry, wounded at New Georgia, 7 July 1943. They are carrying a M1928A1 Thompson and M1903A1 rifle fitted with a grenade launcher recoil boot.

69th Division soldiers rest in a German bed after weeks in the open, 14 March, 1945. Note the two M3's.

Men of the 24th Infantry Division in the Philippines. Notice the Thompson Submachine Gun M1928A1.

SUBMACHINE GUNS

The term "submachine gun" is used in the United States to designate those weapons known in Europe as "machine pistols"—which is, perhaps, more accurate descriptive nomenclature.

Guns of this type are used by all the warring nations and are considered essential equipment for such shock units as paratroopers and commando groups which engage at close range and under conditions where success may depend upon intensely concentrated fire power swiftly and accurately delivered.

GUN, SUBMACHINE, CALIBER .45, M3

Standard in the Army of the United States in 1944 was the Submachine Gun, Caliber .45, M3. No better exemplification could be found of the statement that the American soldier is the best equipped fighting man in the world. The gun itself is remarkable, but even more noteworthy is the circumstance that it was in production within less than one year from July 1942 when the Technical Division of the Ordnance Department authorized the development of a weapon of its particular type.

The Submachine Gun M3 is a caliber .45 weapon weighing 8 pounds, 15 ounces, complete with magazine, oiler, and sling. Its over-all length is 29.8 inches, which is shortened to 22.8 inches when the extension stock—which may be used in emergency as a cleaning rod—is closed. The 230-grain ball of the caliber .45, M1 cartridge is projected through an 8-inch barrel rifled with four right-hand twist grooves. The pitch, or twist, is one turn in 16 inches. An alternative rifling of one turn in 15 inches is permitted the manufacturer.

The gun operates upon the straight blowback principle, the fixed firing pin in the heavy bolt firing the cartridge at the completion of the forward stroke. The major portion of the energy of the explosion is thus absorbed by the inertia of the bolt. When this is overcome, the remaining energy of the explosion is sufficient to drive the bolt to the rear against the compression of the operating springs. The fired case is ejected on the retracting stroke and the compressed dual springs furnish power to return the bolt to the firing position, picking up and chambering another round on its forward movement.

Gun, Submachine, Caliber .45, M3

The use of a heavy bolt holds the cyclic rate of fire of the M3 to approximately 400 rounds per minute. This low rate of fire and the design which places the heel of the stock in almost a straight line with the axis of the bore combine to reduce recoil, virtually to eliminate muzzle-climb, and to produce unusual accuracy whether the weapon be used with stock extended or as a "two-hand" pistol.

Although made for U. S. service in caliber .45, the Submachine Gun M3, may be converted to a 9-mm weapon by substituting a barrel of that caliber, a replacement bolt and a magazine adapter—an operation requiring but a few minutes and accomplished without tools. Thus converted it will handle not only the 9-mm British standard cartridge but will also function with captured German, 9-mm Parabellum rounds. These conversion components are not standard and it should be emphasized that the M3 will not function with all 9-mm pistol cartridges. The Parabellum is loaded for several German and Italian service weapons, but the 9-mm cartridge is as popular on the Continent as the caliber .38 in America and is loaded in many case sizes and bullet weights. Cartridges longer than the 1.18 inches of the Parabellum will not fit in the M3 magazine or chamber, satisfactory functioning of the shorter 9-mm cartridge is problematical, to say the least.

A special 9-mm semi-armor-piercing cartridge is loaded for the German Schmeisser pistol. Use of those high velocity loads would not be safe in an arm other than one designed for the increased pressures developed.

Thompson Submachine Gun M1928A1
50-Round Drum Magazine

The program for the development of the submachine gun called for the manufacture of pilot models of two weapons, one of caliber .45, and the other of 9-mm, but the simpler device of interchangeable barrels and other parts was recognized and suggested by the Ordnance Department.

Stampings are used wherever possible in the manufacture of the M3; only the barrel, bolt, and a few additional components require machining operations, no critical metals are employed, and the gun may be turned out by production-line methods at a minimum cost for a weapon of this type. The barrel, for example, is produced by a simple, speedy, and inexpensive swaging operation.

The many achievements represented by the Submachine Gun M3 can be better appreciated by a brief description of the Thompson Submachine Gun M1928A1, which was Standard on 6 February 1941 when the original program for a more satisfactory weapon of this type—a program which led to the development of the M3—was undertaken.

In its existing form the Thompson represented 20 years development since it was patented in 1920. It was an air-cooled weapon operated by delayed blowback and equipped with a walnut stock for firing from the shoulder. It was fitted with a compensator. Bolt, receiver, and barrel groups required precision machining to close tolerances and virtually all parts of the gun called for the employment of skilled operators and for the use of metals which even as early as 1940 were recognized as critical.

The Submachine Gun M3 can be stripped for convenient stowing in a soldier's pack, for shipment, or for packing in standard containers to be dropped by parachute. The barrel and magazine are removed and the extension stock is folded. The gun stripped occupies a space 12 5/8 inches long, 7 3/8 inches high, and 3 1/8 inches deep—or 291 cubic inches.

The following significant reference to the M3 Gun is quoted from the Second Summary Report of the Aberdeen Proving Ground on all submachine guns tested up to 10 April 1943; "Although it would be dangerous to state that further improvements and developments are unlikely, the ultimate has been reached in this type of weapon for the time being and production may begin without fear of immediate change."

That conclusion was reached at the end of the long series of tests, which led to the adoption of the Submachine Gun M3. Not until such an assertion could be made was production ordered. Before discussing development of the Submachine Gun M3 and exhaustive tests of that weapon conducted by the Ordnance Department, it would be well to sketch the general background of the submachine gun, a chapter in the larger history of the demand for fire power and still more fire power to be placed at the command of the fighting man.

Neither any one weapon nor the progressive developments of any one inventor may be designated as the prototype of the submachine gun. Its roots extend to the last decade of the 19th century when the Borchardt pistol, the first self-operated handgun in history, was perfected by a Connecticut inventor, Borchardt, who had been associated in the manufacture of the famous Sharps rifles. The Borchardt pistol was manufactured commercially as early as 1893 by the Loewe Arms Company of Germany and eventually became the Luger or Parabellum pistol, familiar as the standard side arm of the German Army during World War I. The Luger still retains the toggle-breech mechanism and recoil operation, which were features of the original Borchardt.

The next few years saw the development of the first Bergmann automatic pistol, the Steyr-Mannlicher, the Schwarzlose, and many others, which never progressed beyond the experimental stage.

Demand for increased firepower brought about minor changes in the Mauser design of 1896 pistol. Such minor changes included a detachable box magazine to replace the original clip-loaded cartridge well and a selector to permit semi- and full-automatic fire. During World War I a recoil operated carbine, semi- and full-automatic fire known as the Bergmann "Muskete," the compact Villa-Perosa 9-mm Italian gun, and the Beretta carbine appeared in the hands of German and Italian troops. The Beretta—used with but slight changes in the Italian Army today—is a machine carbine, which differs but slightly from many submachine guns which followed a decade later. In this model the faulty design is best shown by the

Original caption reads "Guadalcanal". The Marine Tanker standing in front of his M3A1 Stuart tank holds a Model 1928A1 Thompson submachine gun with drum magazine and a holstered .45.

"Guadalcanal August 1942". The Marine has at the ready a Thompson Model 1928A1 with drum magazine. The machine gun at center is a Browning M1919A4 with air-cooled barrel.

A Marine cradling his M1 Thompson.

Marine Corps Historical Center
Photo by PFC Robert E. Keller

"Herded atop a tank, Marine Infantrymen are rushed to the town of Ouga, on Okinawa."
The bottom center Marine holds a M1928A1 Thompson with box magazine, the rest M1 Garands.

Marine Corps Historical Center

"Tarawa, Nov. 20-23, 1943. Marines preparing to advance on West Beach". The right two Marines carry Model 1928A1 Thompsons.

Marine Corps Historical Center

"Okinawa, 4 May 45, Marines assault a ridge supported by bazookas. This action took place two miles north of Naha." Even as late as 1945 a drum-fed Thompson was desired and used.

fact that the coil spring and bolt rod were exposed for the major portion of their length. Dirt and foreign matter had easy access to the gun's action and malfunctions were frequent.

The demand for fire power and still more fire power to be placed at the command of infantry troops and of shock units greatly stimulated interest in the development of light automatic or semi-automatic weapons during the years which followed World War I. The famous "Tommy Gun" was patented in 1920 and was standardized in the United States Army as the Submachine Gun, Thompson, M1928. In its original form the Thompson was fed from drum magazines of 50- and 100-round capacity. A 20-round box magazine drum was also supplied.

On the continent, German ordnance designers were active in the development of a machine pistol. The Bergmann "Muskete" was subject to various improvements and modifications, which later appeared in the Schmeisser and the Steyr-Solothurn, Solothurn, and Neuhausen guns. The Mauser pistol, 7.63-mm, modified as previously mentioned, placed this weapon in the category of submachine guns, although it was far more complicated than was desirable.

Finnish designers produced the Soumi. The Russian Degtyarov was a modification of the German Bergmann. In spite of the many "machine pistols," all the guns developed during that period were actually light, short-barreled, automatic rifles. The pioneer models of the Schmeisser and other foreign weapons were equally as heavy as the M1928A1 Thompson, weighing practically 11 pounds. All of these weapons were designed as shoulder weapons and were equipped with fixed wood stocks of con-

**Thompson Submachine Gun M1928A1
with 30-Round Box Magazine**

ventional length and drop, and thus were virtually useless as cavalry weapons; the drum and side feeding magazines created a shifting center of gravity; they were too long for convenient stowage as auxiliary arms in tanks or vehicles, and, as was to be learned, entirely too bulky for use by parachute troops.

The Blitzkrieg of 1940 introduced a new weapon. German paratroopers and motorcycle units carried a new, short Schmeisser weighing 8.25 pounds and equipped with a skeleton stock which when folded reduced the over-all length of the arm to 24.5 inches. It was fully automatic in action and fired a 9-mm cartridge from a 32-round magazine.

The high efficiency and serviceability of the Schmeisser as demonstrated under combat conditions greatly stimulated interest in weapons of that type. Tests conducted by the Ordnance Department of the M1928A1 Thompson Infantry gun proved that such expensive devices as muzzle brakes and compensators (used to prevent or reduce any tendency of the weapon to climb under full-automatic fire) were unnecessary so long as the recoil could be kept closely parallel to the center line of the stock.

The using arms, infantry and cavalry, were then called upon for an expression of the characteristics

101st Airborne on way to Bastogne, Belgium, 12/19/1944. Note the Thompson on Jeep hood.

Soldiers of the 9th Division being shelled in Geich, Germany on 12/11/1944, are sheltered behind a tank. The Thompson M1 is at the ready. Bill Mauldin's Willie and Joe would understand this picture and their thoughts.

desired in a submachine gun and expressed their respective requirements as follows:

	Infantry Requirements	Cavalry Requirements
Caliber	.30 or .45	.30 or .45
Cooling	Air	Air
Weight	7 to 10 lbs.	Not more than 11 lbs.
Length	36 in.	34 in.
Length without stock or with stock folded	23 in.	Removable or Folding stock not essential
Sights	Open	Open, adjustable
Magazine capacity	50 rds.	20 and 50 rds.
Rate of fire	500 rds. per min.	600 rds. per min.
Type of fire	Automatic and semi-automatic	Automatic and semi-automatic
Grip	Pistol	Pistol
Sling	Yes	Yes
Max. effective range	300 yd.	300 yd.

These suggestions were used as an aid in preparing design specifications called for in a blowback-operated weapon using the caliber .45, M1911 cartridge, so designed that the breech remained closed until pressures fell below a point that might endanger or inconvenience the operator.

The weight, less magazine, was not to exceed 8 pounds; the maximum length permissible was 35 inches. The weapon should be equipped with a safety device, have a cyclic rate of 600 ± 50 rounds per minute, and be capable of either full-automatic or semi-automatic fire. The last provision was later amended, semi-automatic fire control being found unnecessary. Further specifications directed that it should be possible to change magazines with the bolt in either the open or closed position.

At the recommendation of the Aberdeen Proving Ground several amendments were made in those specifications. The new requirements were that the bolt or breechblock should be as heavy as possible; the cyclic rate should not exceed 500 rounds per minute, and not less than 90 percent of the shots fired

90

full-automatic from a standing position should strike a 6- x 6-foot target at 50 yards.

Manufacturing and production details were also studied. The United States was still a nonbelligerent during the 18 months which followed the invasion of the Low Countries and the fall of France, but it was realized that American industry might be called upon at any time to supply equipment and replacements for huge armies. In those circumstances, all items including submachine guns would have to be reduced to a production-line basis and no consideration could be given to weapons, which required elaborate and expensive machining operations.

The requirements issued called for an all-metal gun, fabricated as far as possible from stamped parts to permit speed and economy of production and to require a minimum of machine operations and use little or no critical metal. Design was further simplified by eliminating any requirements for a sling or sling swivels as well as any; selector device permitting full-automatic fire. A single-speed, full-automatic weapon with a low cyclic rate would be acceptable.

As a first step toward the desired end, the guns of the Thompson series were studied with a view to their simplification. A minor change worthy of note was that breakage and splitting of stocks were overcome by incorporating a "through-bolt" in the design of guns of this series. The through-bolt extends across the stock at its forward end to prevent splitting.

USAMHI
Photo by T/S A.H. Herz

"Crossing the Rhine at Oberessel, Germany, 89th Division men crouch low in their crowded assault boat to escape enemy fire. 3/26/45. 89th Infantry Division, U.S. 3rd Army." **The GI on top with the watch has a Thompson M1. On left is a BAR, in center a M1 Carbine, the rest have Garand rifles, with the center left having a grenade launcher. The contributing author's Uncle John E. Green, 5th Div., 11th Regt. said the Rhine was his easiest river crossing — "didn't have to row".**

GUN, SUBMACHINE, CALIBER .45, THOMPSON, M1

Thompson Submachine Gun M1

Further development produced the Submachine Gun, Thompson, M1, which was far simpler than its immediate predecessors. The compensator was eliminated, the cooling fins disappeared from the barrel; and the elaborate, complicated, and expensive locking mechanism was replaced by the simpler action of a heavy bolt. Production of the new gun required fewer operations at a saving of more than 25 dollars per unit. The weight remained unchanged, however, and the stock was still of the conventional rigid design. The weapon was still far short of the goal desired for mass production.

A modification of the M1 and M1A1 offered further simplification. In these guns the firing pin was machined integrally with the bolt, a step which eliminated the firing pin, firing pin spring, hammer, and hammer spring. Tests conducted at Springfield Armory and Aberdeen Proving Ground indicated that the functioning of the modified weapon was superior to that of the M1. Manufacture was simplified by the elimination of the deep drilling operation necessary to accommodate those moving parts within the bolt and cost of production was still further reduced.

The sequence of models can be best presented by considering the Hyde and Hyde-Inland weapons. The gun here identified as Hyde 109 was the first submachine gun designed by George J. Hyde and was subjected to tests at Aberdeen Proving Ground between 5 and 27 October and on 21 November 1939. A total of 1,534 rounds were fired.

The gun was a straight blowback weapon firing the U.S. Caliber .45, M1911 cartridge through an

"Americans of Japanese descent of the 100th Infantry Battalion, 34th Division, Fifth Army examine a still smoldering German vehicle, after entering Leghorn, Italy, which they helped to capture. July 19, 1944". The crouching Nisei GI is holding a M1 Thompson submachine gun.

Hyde 109 Submachine Gun

11.25-inch barrel finned for cooling and fitted with a compensator. The 20- or 40-round magazines were inserted from below. There was no forestock, but a pistol foregrip was mounted below the barrel. The cocking piece was exposed, and its movement with each shot was approximately 0.5 inch toward the gunner's eye. While there was little danger of actual injury, the feature presented a mental hazard and was objectionable. Muzzle flash, bright yellow in color, was pronounced.

After each of the four dust and mud tests to which it was subjected, the Hyde 109 functioned normally except for failure to feed caused by dirt blocking a weak magazine spring. It was necessary to clean the Thompson M1928, after each test to restore normal functioning.

The Hyde 109 was judged far superior to the Thompson under adverse conditions of mud and dust, its functioning components were less complicated, it cooled more rapidly after full-automatic fire, handled more easily, and it had a lighter recoil.

The design of the trigger groups was not satisfactory: the visible rearward motion of the exposed cocking piece was objectionable, the magazine springs were weak, the flanges on the bolt face could be cracked or broken by falling on an empty chamber, and the forward grip was inadequately supported.

Service test of the gun in its existing form was not warranted. It was redesigned and a new gun, identified here as the Hyde-Inland I, was submitted to Aberdeen and tested on 2, 9, 10, 15 April 1943. All of the objectionable characteristics of the pilot model of the series Hyde 109 had been eliminated. The action had been completely enclosed and there were no external moving parts to disturb the operator or to catch in his clothing. Barrel fins had been removed and the stock extended to enclose the barrel and protect the operator's hand. The straight blowback action was the same and the weapon was capable of either semi- or full-automatic fire, controlled by a selector. Bolt and firing pin were a unit. The gun was lighter than either the Hyde 109 or the Thompson, M1928A1.

At a range of 50 yards in full-automatic fire from the offhand position, the Hyde Inland I placed 99 of 100 shots upon the 6- x 6-foot target. This compared with 50 hits from the M1 and 49 from the M1928A1. Those who fired the subject gun stated that it handled very well, that the recoil was soft, and that there was no appreciable tendency to climb under full-automatic fire.

The subject gun was fired 6,080 rounds in the endurance tests. There were 20 malfunctions, 15 being failures of the bolt to remain open after the last round was fired. On three occasions the bolt remained open but closed when the magazine was withdrawn. The other malfunctions were one light firing pin blow and one failure to feed.

The average cyclic rate was 527 rounds per minute. That of the Thompson, M1928A1, was 610, that of the M1 was 775. The result of the mud and dust tests indicated some superiority over the Thompson. The conclusions reached were that the Hyde-Inland I was superior in accuracy to the MI and M1928AI in full-automatic fire from a machine rest, but that it was poor in comparison with the control weapons in offhand, semi-automatic fire. Consequently, five Hyde-Inland 2 guns embodying minor modifications were tested for functioning in June 1942. As a result of this test it was recommended that this model gun with a heavy operating spring and slight redesign of the magazine well, was adopted as Substitute Standard in April 1942 and designated as Gun, Submachine, Caliber .45, M2.

GUN, SUBMACHINE, CALIBER .45, M2

In view of the tremendous requirements for submachine guns at that time it was not considered advisable to convert existing facilities to the manufacture of the new weapon and an attempt was made to produce the M2 by awarding contracts to firms not then engaged in war work. Many difficulties were encountered, as was anticipated, and actual production models of the M2 did not reach Aberdeen until May 1943, 5 months after the M3 had been standardized. Production of the M2 was discontinued.

During the period which covered the modification of the Thompson guns and the adoption of the M2 as a Substitute Standard item, more than 20 submachine guns of American and foreign manufacture were tested at Aberdeen Proving Ground.

Submachine Gun, Caliber .45, M2

All but a few were given the complete service test and the majority proved quite unfit for military use. With the exception of the Atmed, none would function satisfactorily under adverse mud conditions—a fault shared by the models then classified as U. S. Army Standard—and virtually all presented intricacies of design, which forbade manufacture by production-line methods. The most general fault observed was an excessive cyclic rate, which resulted in a marked tendency to climb under full-automatic fire. In the hands of inexperienced operators some guns were firing almost vertically by the time the last round in the magazine had been reached.

Still further simplification was essential. The records of the tests and the weapons themselves were carefully studied by officers of the Ordnance Department. Reports of the use of submachine guns in combat and in commando operations crystallized further the concept of the basic requirements for such a weapon—reliability, simplicity, compactness to permit packaging in small containers, and a low cyclic rate. The magazine should have a capacity of at least 25 rounds and should be inserted from below.

The only advantage of the side-feeding magazines, such as used in the British Sten, was in firing from the prone position; the disadvantages of such a feed were many.

Designs were prepared and specifications submitted to a firm of long experience in the production of stamped parts. That contractor agreed to make a production study of the Sten gun with a view to making a comparable weapon.

The gun was originally designated T15. The specifications were amended to provide for a caliber .45 weapon which would fire 9-mm ammunition by substitution of a lighter bolt, a magazine adapter, and a 9-mm barrel. The Sten magazine would be used with the modified weapon. Further simplification elimi-

nated the requirement for a selector providing for semi-automatic as well as full-automatic fire. The modified weapon was designated T20.

Five pilot models of the T20 were tested at Aberdeen Proving Ground on 18, 19, and 24 November 1942. These were straight blowback weapons weighing 7.66 pounds in caliber .45 without magazines and 7.74 pounds when converted to 9-mm caliber. The cyclic rate of fire was approximately 400 rounds per minute and there was little or no tendency of the muzzle to climb. The guns were not equipped with selectors and semi-automatic fire could be approximated only by a quick release of the trigger after each shot.

The following performance of other submachine guns fired full-automatic at 50 yards range, may be compared with the T20 which placed 97 out of 100 shots on 6- x 6- foot target:

Thompson, M1, Cal. .45..................................89
Thompson, M1928A1, Cal. .45 93
M2, Cal. .45...84
Schmeisser, 9-mm 81
Sten, Mk. II, 9-mm. 94

A total of 5,000 rounds were fired from the caliber .45, in an endurance test. Brass cases were used. There were two failures to feed, both caused by the follower sticking in the magazine well. There were three failures to eject; and one failure to feed in the firing of 500 rounds of steel-cased ammunition.

Twenty-three failures to eject occurred during the firing of 5,000 rounds of 9-mm ammunition. The ejection port was too small. When the port was enlarged, 1,250 rounds were fired with no ejection failures.

The T20, when submitted to dust and mud tests, performed far superior to that of any other submachine gun submitted to any such tests.

The final conclusions were confirmed by further tests conducted independently by the Airborne Command (Fort Bragg, North Carolina), the Amphibious Warfare Board (Fort Carrabelle, Florida), the Infantry Board (Fort Benning, Georgia), and the Armored Force Board (Fort Knox, Kentucky). Those using arms were unanimous in their approval of the weapon and in their requests that it be standardized and placed in production immediately.

The Airborne Command reported the gun suitable for use by parachute troops. Twelve packaged

T20's would fit into the standard A5 aerial delivery container for dropping by parachute. The only malfunctions during the firing of 385 rounds were caused by faulty design of the magazine.

The report of the Amphibious Warfare Board was in general agreement with that of Aberdeen Proving Ground. The gun was tested under simulated landing conditions. After being fired from a landing boat at targets, on shore, it was dropped into the surf, picked up, and fired again. Functioning was satisfactory throughout the tests. Malfunctions in the firing of 265 rounds were caused by the jamming of the magazine follower.

The Infantry Board also suggested changes in the magazine. A total of 3,014 rounds were fired in the course of seven tests. The report of the Armored Force agreed with that of other using arms. The gun was found to be a better auxiliary arm for tank troops than any other standard sub-machine gun. A total of 3,558 rounds were fired at Fort Knox.

**ADOPTION OF THE
GUN, SUBMACHINE, CALIBER .45, M3**

On 24 December 1942, the Ordnance Committee recommended the gun for standardization as the M3. The Ordnance Department took the best that American ingenuity and resourcefulness could offer; neither sentiment nor military conservatism were permitted to influence decisions, the goal was "the ultimate in a weapon of this type" and the M3 is the achievement of that objective.

The scope of the research and experimentation conducted by the Ordnance Department is revealed by the long list of foreign and domestic submachine guns tested in the course of the project. The principal characteristics of those weapons appear in tabular form herewith.

SUBMACHINE GUN	CALIBER	WEIGHT LBS.	LENGTH INCHES	MAGAZINE CAPACITY	ACTION	CYCLIC RATE
Atlantic	.38 ACP	8.78	35.25	30	Del. b.b.	508
Atmed	.45	9.48	33.6	25	b.b.	524
Austen	9-mm	8.54	33.5	30	b.b.	575
Bergmann	9-mm	9.00	33.5	32	b.b.	-
Hi-Standard	.45	8.75	33.1	20	b.b.	880
Hyde 109	.45	9.50	35.0	20-40	b.b.	762
Hyde-lnland (M2)	.45	9.08	33.9	20-50	b.b.	527
Olsen	.45	9.22	33.5	20	b.b.	1,111
Owen	9-mm	10.04	32.0	33	b.b.	812
Reising-1	.45	7.07	35.0	18	Del. b.b.	450
Reising-2	.45	7.37	35.75	20	b.b.	750
Schmeisser*	9-mm	8.25	35.0	32	b.b.	-
Smith & Wesson	9-mm	8.20	33.8	20	b.b.	SEMI
Star	9-mm	8.20	35.4	10-30	Del. b.b.	700
Sten Mk. III	9-mm	7.19	-	30	b.b.	3-700
Suomi	9-mm	10.50	33.8	20-25	b.b.	537
Thompson, M1928A1	.45	10.80	31.8	20-50	Del. b.b.	833
Thompson, M1	.45	9.50	33.69	20-30	b.b.	775
Thompson, T2	.45	8.60	-	20	b.b.	600
Turner (gas)	.45	5.32	-	20	Gas	1483
United Defense**	9-mm/.45	7.96	32.0	25	b.b.	1150
Woodhull	.45	8.12	33.5	10	b.b.	760

Del. b.b.—Delayed blowback   b.b.—Blowback   Gas—Gas operated

*The Schmeisser gun, a German weapon, was tested for purposes of study and not in competition with standard or subject gun.

**The United Defense was convertible, 9-mm to cal. .45 by substitution of barrel. Barrel not in use served as an extension stock.

**Smith & Wesson
Submachine Gun 9-mm
Pilot Model and Ammunition**

SMITH & WESSON 9-MM SUBMACHINE GUN

The Smith & Wesson Submachine Gun was inspected and fired at Aberdeen Proving Ground, November 1939. This weapon was of the straight blowback type utilizing a 20-round magazine inserted from below. No compensator or muzzle brake was used since there was no provision for full-automatic fire. The British Government contracted for this rifle, known as the Model 1940 Light Rifle. However, after a thousand had been delivered functioning problems were discovered with British 9mm ammo and the contract was cancelled.

REISING SUBMACHINE GUN

The first Reising Submachine Gun manufactured by the Harrington and Richardson Arms Company was tested in July 1941. It was a delayed blowback weapon with a manually operated fire control slide, which could be placed in three positions for safety, semi- and full-automatic fire. The recoil was lighter, but the gun had a tendency to climb even when short bursts were fired, and was frequently off the target after only four rounds. The gun failed to fire during sand, mud, and dust tests. This weapon, with some minor corrections was resubmitted for test in November 1941 and was tested in competition with the Thompson, M1928A1. The Armored Force Board, after testing this gun stated that it was satisfactory for Armored Force use and that the folding stock was desired, and therefore recommended that it be adopted and that at least 1,000 be purchased for extended service tests.

**Reising Submachine Gun, Model 55
Caliber .45, with Collapsible Stock**

**Reising Submachine Gun Model 50
Caliber .45, Standard Wooden Stock**

The report of the Infantry Board, submitted a month later, was more cautious. That Board concluded that the Reising had distinct possibilities and should be retested after the manufacturer had corrected certain minor faults. It was found that small springs and screws were easily lost, that screws worked loose during firing, and that the extractor could not be cleaned in the field but required shop facilities, and that the magazine "would not function under field conditions."

The Cavalry Board found the gun suitable and asked for 50 of them equipped with oiling kits. Classification as Substitute Standard was recommended.

The Reising was also tested by the Navy Department and the Marine Corps. Unofficial information states that 70,000 were purchased, with an additional large quantity by the Coast Guard.

Harrington & Richardson Reising Manual

**H&R Reising Submachine Guns
Models 50 and 55, Caliber .45
being inspected by the Marine Corps.**

**Harrington & Richardson, Reising Model 60
.45 Caliber, Semi-Automatic Rifle
1700 were bought by the Defense Supplies
Corporation, a U.S. Federal Agency,
for guard use at war production plants.**

A procurement of 1700 Semi-automatic Model 60
Reising rifles were bought by the Defense Supplies
Corporation, a Federal Agency chartered to support
war mobilization, for issue to plant guards.

**Coast Guard "Dog Beach Patrol, Parramore
Beach.", 21 October 1943. Reising Model 50.**

**Reising Model 55 folding stock machine gun
fired by a Marine at a Marine training base.**

**Marines in training. Left; Reising Model 55, with
a folding stock. Right; Reising Model 50.**

**Reising Submachine Gun, Model 55
Caliber .45, with Collapsible Stock, left view**

**Surrender of German submarine U-858, May
1945 on ATR-57 off Cape May, New Jersey. The
Marine guard holds a Model 50 Reising.**

U.S. Coast Guard Port Security

Arms from left include:
M1903 Rifle with 1905 bayonet,
M1896 Colt machine gun,
Browning Automatic Rifle,
M1896 Colt "Potato Digger",
1928A1 Thompson with drum,
Reising Model 50 machine gun,
M1903 Rifle with 1905 bayonet,
M1903 Rifle with 1905 bayonet,
Reising Model 50 machine gun,
M1903 Rifle with 1905 bayonet,
M1903 Rifle with 1905 bayonet,
M1903 Rifle with 1905 bayonet.

U.S. Coast Guard Historian's Office

Marine Corps Historical Center

"When not fighting they clean their weapons. The soldier on left made me promise to caption this photo "A Marine cleans his Reising Gun". He said "I'm a Marine now, not a soldier." Guadalcanal, November 1942. The Marines' weapons from left are a Reising Model 55 with folding metal stock, Reising Model 50 with conventional stock, and on right a .30 caliber BAR. The contributing author's Uncle William R. Miller served with the 3rd Division on Guadalcanal.

**Suomi 9-mm
Submachine Gun**

SUOMI 9-MM SUBMACHINE GUN

The Suomi 9-mm Submachine Gun is a Finnish development and was tested at Aberdeen Proving Ground in July 1940. It is a straight blowback operated weapon with a selector to permit semi- and full-automatic fire and has a 25-round magazine inserted from below.

Direct comparison between the Suomi and the Thompson M1928A1 Submachine Gun was difficult because of the difference in calibers. The Suomi is simpler in design and may be disassembled more easily. It is slightly more effective than the Thompson under adverse conditions of dust and mud. The recoil is less because of the lighter cartridge. It is heavier than the Thompson by 0.7 pound, and has a greater tendency to climb in automatic fire. Due to the gun's use of ammunition not standard in the U.S. Army, the Suomi was not recommended for service test.

STAR SUBMACHINE GUN

The Star submachine gun was designed by Sr. Jose Cunill de Figuerola and submitted by the Star Company. It was tested in competition with the Thompson, M1928A1 on 23 and 24 August 1940.

It is a 9-mm delayed blowback weapon weighing 8 pounds, 2 ounces, and measuring 25.4 inches over-all.

The barrel is finned for cooling and is covered with a slotted jacket. The magazine is of 10- or 30-round capacity and inserted from below. The gun is equipped with a compensator.

Two levers on the left side of the receiver control the firing rate. The forward lever may be positioned for low speed (300 rpm) full-automatic fire or for single shot operation. The rear lever has three positions: semi-automatic, high speed (700 rpm) full-automatic, and safe.

The muzzle flash of this weapon was very noticeable and sparks were observed at the breech end around the bolt. Recoil was very light and there was little or no tendency to climb. The gun functioned poorly unless properly lubricated. The only advantages over the Thompson were those of 1.55 pounds lighter weight and the fact that the forward motion of the bolt does not tend to throw the sight off the target as with the Thompson. This gun was not recommended for service test.

ATMED SUBMACHINE GUN

This weapon was designed by George J. Hyde and submitted by Atmed Manufacturing Company. It is a caliber .45 weapon weighing 9.48 pounds and operating on the straight blowback principle. No compensator or muzzle brake is used. The 11.5-inch barrel is provided with cooling fins. A lever on the left side of the trigger guard may be positioned for safety, full-automatic, and semi-automatic fire. The Atmed was tested at Aberdeen Proving Ground on 3, 7 September 1940.

The Atmed is designed on the Becker principle, in which the cartridge is ignited before the heavy bolt has ceased its forward motion. This serves to dampen recoil but when ignition is too early, pressure is lost and the bolt fails to recoil a sufficient distance to pick up and chamber another round. When first tested, the gun functioned very poorly with Frankford Arsenal

**Star Submachine Gun
Caliber 9-mm**

**Atmed Submachine Gun
Caliber .45**

ammunition, repeated jams being caused by primers which had been punched completely from their cases. Somewhat more satisfactory functioning was obtained with commercial ammunition and the difficulty virtually disappeared when the firing pin was shortened 0.009 inch, permitting a further forward travel of the bolt before ignition of the cartridge.

A weak sear bar spring was judged to be the cause of erratic performance in semi-automatic fire. At times the gun failed to fire, at other times it would fire doublets and triplets when the trigger was depressed. Shortening of the driving spring by 1 3/8 inches failed to correct this fault. The over-all results of test of this item indicated that it did not warrant being subjected to service test.

HI-STANDARD SUBMACHINE GUN

The first model of the Hi-Standard Submachine Gun was inspected and informally tested at Aberdeen Proving Ground on 28 and 29 August 1940. It was a caliber .45 weapon weighing 8.75 pounds and measuring 33.1 inches over-all.

In the functioning tests the Hi-Standard handled more easily than the Thompson, M1928A1, and was of simpler construction. The cyclic rate of 900 rounds per minute was high and there was no provision for a magazine of more than 20-round capacity.

Further tests were recommended and the gun was returned to the manufacturers who submitted a second model on 12 November 1941. The gun was formally tested at Aberdeen Proving Ground on 24 and 26 November 1941. A 40-round magazine accompanied the weapon but could not be used because the forestock had been moved about 1.5 inches to the rear to provide a more convenient grip in prone firing. The average cyclic rate—880 rounds per minute—was only slightly lower than that of the earlier model.

Conclusions reached as a result of the tests of the Hi-Standard gun were that its accuracy from machine rest was good in comparison with the Thompson,

M1928A1, its accuracy from the offhand position, full-automatic, was very good in comparison with the Thompson, M1928A1, and excellent in comparison with the Reising gun. Accuracy was rather poor when fired offhand, semi-automatic. The gun's functioning was excellent under adverse dust conditions, good under excessive mud. General functioning was good. The only common malfunction was that of firing doublets in semi-automatic operation. This appeared to be due to the rather inferior quality of the sear spring, which took a permanent set after several hundred rounds. The gun was well balanced and well made. The recoil was light and there was little tendency to climb in full-automatic fire. No muzzle brake was used.

Six Hi-Standard guns were distributed among the Infantry Board, Cavalry Board, and Armored Force Board. Limited service tests indicated that further development was necessary before the weapon would meet the requirements of those Arms. The classification of the M2 as Substitute Standard halted further tests of the Hi-Standard gun. A number of these arms are believed to have been purchased by the OSS for distribution to resistance forces.

WOODHULL SUBMACHINE GUN

The Woodhull Corporation submitted their first weapon for test as a carbine. This was a caliber .30 weapon built on the frame of the Winchester Model 1907 self-loading rifle, caliber .351.

In building a submachine gun, the makers used the heavier frame of the Winchester Model 1910 self-loading rifle, chambered commercially for the caliber .401 cartridge. The caliber was increased to .45 and provision made for a 10-round magazine, inserted from below.

Woodhull adaptation of the Winchester self-loading mechanism to full-automatic fire necessitated an extremely complicated fire selector, difficult to dismount or assemble. It cannot be changed from the semi-automatic to the full-automatic position unless the bolt is retracted.

Hi-Standard Submachine Gun, Caliber .45

Woodhull Submachine Gun, Caliber .45

The gun has a straight blowback action; a compensator is used, and the barrel is finned for cooling.

The gun was tested for accuracy, general functioning and functioning under adverse conditions, on 15 and 16 January 1942. A total of 413 rounds were fired.

The Woodhull was a well made and well finished weapon but in certain details extremely complicated and not adaptable to quantity production. The excessively loud report was objectionable. The magazines as designed were not suited for rapid charging and were liable to cause malfunctions. The operation was poor under extreme conditions of mud. (The Thompson, M1928A1 is very poor). No recommendations for further tests were made.

STEN 9-MM MK. II

This 9-mm, 7.19-pound weapon is a British development and is the standard submachine gun of the British armies. The Mk. I, Mk. II, and Mk. III Sten guns differ only in minor details. All are straight blowback weapons with 30-round magazines feeding from the left side. The firing pin and bolt are integral and the cartridge is picked up, chambered, and fired on the closing stroke.

Tests of many submachine guns at Aberdeen Proving Ground indicated that the side-feeding magazine is not a desirable feature on weapons of this type. The weight of the full magazine imparts considerable torsional strain upon the forward hand and some operators have noticed a disturbance of aim due to a shifting center of gravity as the magazine is fired. The operating spring of the Sten is exposed for the greater part of its length by the open slot in which the operating knob travels. Foreign material can enter the mechanism. There is no safety and since the bolt cannot be locked—the weapon may be accidentally discharged. Such discharge may occur with the bolt closed if the gun is dropped or the butt plate struck sharply against some solid object.

U.S. Coast Guard Historian's Office

U.S. Coast Guard Port Security Patrol in New York. Left: M1928A1 Thompson with drum.

The Sten is equipped with a selector lever, mounted on the right side of the receiver, permitting full-automatic or semi-automatic fire.

The gun was tested for accuracy, endurance, and general functioning on 23 January 1942. Further tests under adverse conditions of mud and dust and of extreme cold were made on 29 September 1942.

MASCO SUBMACHINE GUN

A submachine gun manufactured by the Masco Ordnance Corporation was shipped to Aberdeen Proving Ground early in April 1942, with the request that it be fired not more than 200 rounds and that a brief and informal report of its merit be sent to the inventor. It was a caliber .45 weapon, blowback operated. The semi-automatic fire control was admittedly inoperative and the gun had no sights. After improvised sights were mounted, 100 rounds were fired at the standard 6- x 6-foot target at 50 yards, offhand. Fifty-seven hits were recorded.

No descriptive record of the weapon was made nor were additional tests attempted. The informal report stated that it was "entirely unfit for military use." The gun was returned to its maker.

Sten Submachine Gun MK. II, Caliber 9-mm

Masco Submachine Gun, Caliber .45

Right View

**Colt Automatic Pistol Caliber .45
with Long Barrel and Shoulder Stock**

COLT PISTOL M1911A1 CONVERTED TO SUBMACHINE GUN

Consideration was given to the two modifications of the standard caliber .45 pistol to convert it to a submachine gun. A modification submitted by Mr. Frank Bielaski was demonstrated to the Chief of Infantry and at his suggestion tested by the Infantry Board to determine its suitability for use by parachute troops. A report upon these tests was to the effect that the modified pistol was greatly inferior to the U. S. Carbine M1 as an auxiliary weapon for infantry and that a carbine with a folding or collapsible stock would more nearly meet the requirements of parachute troops.

The modification submitted by the Colt's Patent Firearms Company had a barrel length increased to approximately 9.5 inches and a perforated sleeve added to facilitate cooling. The long magazine (20-round) is carried in a recess in the extension stock when not in use. The meager and informal report upon this weapon does not state whether any modification of the disconnector of the M1911A1 Pistol was made to permit full-automatic fire, nor is the method of attaching the stock described. It is apparent from the illustration that an operator firing the weapon from the shoulder would be in extreme danger of being struck by the recoiling slide. Equally apparent is the fact that the low mounting of the stock would result in excessive climb under full-automatic fire.

The Ordnance subcommittee recommended (28 May 1942) that development of such modifications of the standard pistol be discontinued.

TURNER SUBMACHINE GUN

This caliber .45 weapon was the only gas-operated submachine gun submitted. Since the Ordnance Department was eager to explore the possibilities of this design in a submachine gun, the Turner was given the standard test at Aberdeen Proving Ground 25 and 28 August 1942.

General observations—The Turner is an extremely lightweight (5.32 pounds without magazine) gas-operated weapon firing the caliber .45, M1911 cartridge, from a 20-round magazine inserted from below.

The gas is taken off from a port on the left side of the barrel a short distance ahead of the chamber. The gas chamber and piston are exposed and present a decided hazard. It would be easy for the fingers of the operator's extended hand to be caught by the moving parts.

The bolt-retracting handle is an integral part of the piston and firing causes it to overheat excessively. Another source of excessive heating is found in the rivets with which the forestock band is attached. Several operators burned their fingers severely.

The bolt failed to remain open after the last shot was fired.

The general functioning was good, but inferior to both the M1 and M2 under excessive dust and would not function under excessive mud.

The extremely high cyclic rate was objectionable.

Considerable carbon escaped from the gas port, blackening the operator's trigger-hand.

The gun was not recommended for further tests.

ATLANTIC SUBMACHINE GUN

The Atlantic submachine gun was a delayed blowback weapon chambered for the caliber .38 automatic Colt pistol cartridge. It was designed by Sr. Jose Cunill de Figuerola, designer of the 9-mm Star gun, and was compared with that arm rather than the Thompson, M1928A1. Tests were made on 28 and 29 August 1942.

The gun was similar in appearance to the Star and incorporated only slight modifications of that weapon. The Star's full-automatic bar, completely depressing the sear, had been eliminated, permitting automatic fire only at a retarded rate. The average cyclic rate was 508 rounds per minute. The Star had a high speed rate of 700 rounds per minute and a retarded rate of 300 rounds. The trigger mechanism of the Star had been simplified in the Atlantic and the magazine catch improved so as to prevent accidental release of the magazine. A foregrip, absent from the Star, appeared on the Atlantic.

The Atlantic demonstrated no particular improvement over the Star gun and was inferior to that weapon in several respects. It was inferior to the M2 in accuracy and in general functioning. In addition, it was chambered for the nonstandard caliber .38 automatic Colt pistol cartridge. The recommendation was that no further consideration be given to the weapon.

AUTO ORDNANCE SUBMACHINE GUN T2

The gun so designated was manufactured by the Auto Ordnance Corp., makers of the Thompson gun, but announced as differing entirely in design from its previous products. Tests were completed at Aberdeen Proving Ground on 11 September 1942.

In competition with the M2, the new gun was found superior only in the mud test. The T2 was operative after immersion in thin mud, while the M2 refused to function after such immersion. The average cyclic rate of the T2 was 600 rounds per minute, that of the M2, 527 rounds. Both weapons were stable under full-automatic fire, but the performance of the M2 was superior.

The selector for full-automatic and semi-automatic fire as supplied on the T2 was neither positive nor reliable and Aberdeen testers expressed the belief that the weapon would be rejected by the using services for that reason.

Accuracy under full-automatic fire was not equal to that of the M2, which scored 99 hits out of 100 shots upon a 6- x 6-ioot target as against 80 hits for the T2. The range at which the tests were fired was not specified but presumably was 50 yards.

In the course of the tests the T2 developed 60 stoppages and 2 breakages as compared with 2 stoppages and no breakages for the M2. It should be mentioned that 37 stoppages of the T2 were attributable to a cracked trigger housing which developed after the firing of 750 rounds. The Ordnance Committee recommended that no further consideration be given to the T2.

36th Infantry Division
Bruyeres, France
20 October 1944
USAMHI

Pfc. Beasel Marbanks of Snyder, Texas with M3 Greasegun and .45 auto. Holster has Texas star.

AUSTEN, MK. I, 9-MM SUBMACHINE GUN

This 9-mm gun is the Australian version of the British Sten and is very similar to that weapon. It is equipped with a foregrip, lacking on the Sten, and a folding stock. The bolt-operating handle, instead of being detachable like that of the Sten, is integral with the bolt. The bolt slot is extended through the receiver to permit the bolt to be withdrawn in disassembly.

In the standard submachine gun test at Aberdeen on 25 - 27 November 1942 the Austen gave a very satisfactory performance as did the majority of the 9-mm weapons tested. The general functioning was considered excellent except for recurrent doublets in semi-automatic fire.

**Auto-Ordnance Submachine Gun T2
Caliber .45**

**Austen Mk. I, Submachine Gun
Caliber 9-mm**

Submachine Gun UD-1
Caliber .45 or 9-mm Interchangeable

Manufactured by
United Defense Supply Corporation
Bayonet Attached
and Spare 9-mm
Barrel Stock Extended

UNITED DEFENSE SUBMACHINE GUN
9-MM OR .45 CALIBER

A submachine gun submitted by the United Defense Corporation was inspected and tested informally at Aberdeen Proving Ground on 2 April 1943. This U.D.-1 was a convertible 9-mm caliber .45 weapon, being adaptable to either cartridge by changing barrels. No change of bolt was necessary. The barrel not in use screwed into a hinged fitting on the left side of the piece above the pistol grip and could be swung to the rear to serve as an extension stock. The position of the pistol grip and the hinged fitting tended to pinch the gunner's thumb.

The gun was of the straight blowback type, equipped with a bayonet, and had a selector on the right side of the receiver with positions for safety, semi-automatic fire and full-automatic fire. There was no satisfactory method of locking the closed bolt. During the test the bolt was closed and the selector placed on safety. The piece was then jarred sharply against a table. The bolt locked and the safety jammed. It was necessary to remove the side plate before the safety could be released.

The gun was not given the complete standard test. A total of 180 rounds of caliber .45 ammunition were fired to test functioning under normal conditions and the performance of the weapon did not warrant an accuracy test. One failure to extract was recorded during the firing. The average cyclic rate was 1,150 rounds per minute which produced a decided tendency to climb. No tests were made with 9-mm ammunition. No further consideration of the United Defense gun was recommended.

It is reported that several thousand United Defense submachine guns were subsequently procured by direction of Office, Strategic Services for distribution to clandestine resistance forces in France. The feature of interchangeable barrels and the ability to use captured German 9-mm caliber ammunition was viewed as desirable from an operations standpoint.

OWEN 9-MM SUBMACHINE GUN

Designed by Lt. Evelyn Owen of the Australian Army, this gun is manufactured in Australia and is standard equipment for the forces of that Commonwealth. It weighs 10.04 pounds, operates on the straight blowback principle, and fires the standard 9-mm British Parabellum cartridge from a 33-round magazine. The magazine feeds from the top and the sights are offset to the right to avoid interference by the rectangular magazine housing.

Fired cases are ejected from below, a decidedly unusual feature being that the ejector is an integral part of the magazine.

Cooling fins are machined on the barrel and the gun is fitted with a compensator. Semi-automatic and full-automatic fire are controlled by a change lever on the left side just above the trigger. When moved to the "Safe" position the change lever blocks the trigger.

The Owen was tested at Aberdeen Proving Ground on 1-4 May 1943 and was rated "good" in accuracy and "excellent" in general functioning, in functioning under the adverse conditions of dust and mud, and in general endurance. The fact that 9-mm ammunition was used throughout the test must be considered in any comparison of the Owen with caliber .45 weapons.

Owen Submachine Gun
9-mm Caliber
with Magazine and Sling

Olsen Submachine Gun   Caliber .45

OLSEN SUBMACHINE GUN

The Olsen Submachine Gun was submitted by A.W. Olsen, its designer, and H.J. Fitzgerald. It is a caliber .45 straight blowback weapon weighing 9.22 pounds with empty 20-round magazine in place. As illustrated below, the receiver of the weapon with the side plate removed shows the extremely light bolt and the unusual curved lip at the top of the magazine. This lip permits the rounds to rise directly into the path of the bolt rather than to be picked up by the bolt on its forward stroke. The result is that the bolt on its forward stroke blocks the magazine and prevents its withdrawal in the event of a malfunction.

Full-automatic fire is obtained by simultaneous pressure upon the trigger and an auxiliary button on the left side of the stock. Semi-automatic fire can be obtained only by depressing and releasing the button, then pulling the trigger. The confusing two-finger process must be repeated for each shot fired. The button is located on the left side of the receiver, immediately behind the trigger, and is within reach of the operator's right thumb as he grasps the pistol grip. Its operation is virtually impossible without releasing or shifting the normal hold upon the piece.

The Olsen gun was tested at Aberdeen on 2 June 1943, and its performance compared with that of the M3. A total of 240 rounds were fired to observe general functioning. The cyclic rate of 1,111 rounds per minute was very high for weapons of this type and the recoil was characterized as "very severe." There was a marked tendency to climb under full-automatic fire. Trigger vibration was so excessive as to produce soreness of the gunner's finger. Changing of the magazine was slow and laborious. The conclusion reached was that the Olsen was far inferior to the M3, and no further action was recommended.

SCHMEISSER, MP 40

This weapon was the standard "Machine Pistol" of the Reichswehr Infantry Parachute troops, and other shock units. It was carried by motorcyclists and as an auxiliary arm in tanks and for crews of ar-

German   Caliber 9-mm
Schmeisser Machine Pistol   M.P. 40

mored vehicles. The designation MP 40- "Maschinenpistole 40"- indicates the year, 1940, in which the model was adopted.

The Schmeisser is a straight blowback weapon weighing 8.87 pounds with empty magazine and firing the standard 9-mm Parabellum cartridge from a 32-round box magazine inserted from below. Its overall length with stock extended is 35 inches, reduced to 24.5 inches by folding the stock. There is no provision for semi-automatic fire and the cyclic rate, full-automatic, as timed at Aberdeen Proving Ground is 519 rounds per minute.

For purposes of comparison with our own and other weapons the Schmeisser was given the standard submachine gun test at Aberdeen between 30 December 1942 and 14 January 1943. U.S. commercial (Winchester) cartridges were used and a total of 5,723 rounds were fired.

It was concluded that the general functioning of the Schmeisser was excellent and that its accuracy was very good. Disassembly and assembly were considerably more complicated than with the M3 and could not be accomplished without tools. On a basis of 100 the Schmeisser was given a rating of 79 as compared with the 95 rating accorded the U.S. Submachine Gun, Caliber .45, M3.

Marine Corps Historical Center   **Okinawa**

Pvt. Bruce Rutherford, Bristol, Tenn. cleaning his M1928A1. The puppies were born on ship.

M3 SUBMACHINE GUN
MINOR MODIFICATIONS

From the foregoing described activities pertaining to the investigation of various submachine guns, it can readily be seen that the simplicity of design of the M3 Submachine Gun lends itself to ready mass production, ease of disassembly and assembly, as well as superiority in functioning over existing types. In preproduction models of the M3 Submachine Gun, made at the Guide Lamp Division of General Motors Corporation, difficulty was encountered with ejection, however, this malfunction was corrected by a slight change in ejection port size, plus a change in extractor protrusion.

In February 1944, reports were received from England to the effect that the retracting lever pawls had proven defective in field use. Examination of the steel used in this component showed it to be the improper type for case hardening in that these pawls were extremely brittle, thus causing them to break adjacent to the rivet hole where the pawl is riveted to the brace. It was further found that breakage and distortion of the retracting lever pawl spring was caused by the spring coming out of its slot in the retracting brace assembly during disassembly and assembly of the weapon. Corrective measures were immediately taken wherein a

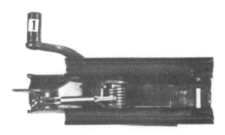

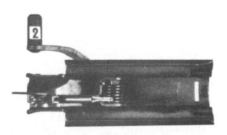

**Modified Cocking Lever Assembly
for Submachine Gun, Caliber .45, M3
(1) Standard.
(2) Modified (Note Addition of
Retracting Lever Pawl Stop at
Rear of Ejector Assembly)**

better grade of steel was used for the retracting lever pawl, plus an increase in width of the metal at the rivet hole. The ejector was modified to incorporate a cocking lever trip on the ejector, and a stop arrangement on the right-hand brace of the retracting lever assembly to prevent the retracting lever pawl from springing forward during disassembly of the housing assembly from the receiver.

A modification to the M3 Submachine Gun was further made to eliminate the possibility of accidental depression of the magazine catch, thus permitting the magazine to drop out of the magazine housing. This modification consisted of supplying a small magazine catch guard and spring to be assembled to the magazine catch. A longer barrel ratchet pad and a change in heat treatment of this component was put into effect to eliminate the wear and facilitate the depression of the pad for removal of the barrel assembly.

GUN, SUBMACHINE, CALIBER .45, M3A1

Although the M3 Submachine Gun in production form appeared to be simplicity of the highest degree, further study by the Ordnance Department indicated the possibility of elimination of the cocking components. To further simplify the gun, as well as its maintenance, a development project was initiated in April 1944 with Guide Lamp for the development and fabrication of six M3E1 Submachine Guns wherein the M3 Submachine Gun was to be modified accordingly:

a. Redesign the housing assembly to eliminate the complete retracting lever assembly.

b. Locate the ejector in the receiver.

c. A new magazine catch to eliminate the possibility of the magazine being released by accidental depression of the magazine catch.

d. New ratchet assembly with an on-off type barrel lock.

e. Rear sight adjustable for manufacturing purposes.

f. Location of oiler in pistol grip.

g. Extension of the ejection port cover rearward.

h. Locate safety rearward on the ejection port cover in order to eliminate operation of the safety on the face of the bolt.

i. Install feed ramp on guide rod locating plate.

j. Change bolt design to incorporate a finger hole for cocking.

106

Naval Historical Center

"Army Commander, Major General George S. Patton with Navy Rear Admiral John L. Hall prepare to go ashore during the North African campaign." "Probably taken on 9 November 1942 when General Patton went ashore for the first time at Fedhala, Morocco. Note Thompson Submachine guns." Also an M1 Carbine next to Patton. The contributing author's Uncle, John E. Green, Co. E, 11th Regiment, 5th Division, 3rd Army firmly believed in "Our Blood — His Guts." His company captured the 1938 Cadillac given to Patton, in which Patton suffered his fatal accident.

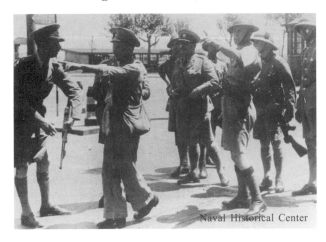

"Shanghai, China. Members of the Shanghai Volunteer Corps on the Bund, August, 1937. Note Thompson Submachine guns."

Naval Historical Center

Assault troops leave an LVT(2) on Morotai, 15 September, 1944. GI carries a M3 Submachine gun.

USAMHI

"13th Mechanized Cavalry Regiment Motorcyclists with Thompson submachine guns, circa 1940." They are riding Harley Davidson motorcycles and they also carry .45 Automatic pistols.

Naval Historical Center

"Manus Island, Admiralties. Men of Troop G, 2nd Squadron, 8th Cavalry on patrol in outrigger canoe," Spring 1944. 3rd right GI carries a Thompson, the rest M1 Carbines.

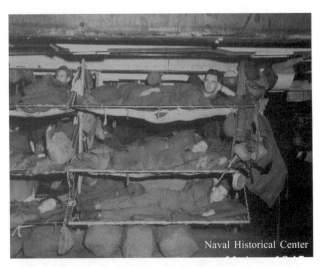

Naval Historical Center

Marines on transport Brazil enroute to the Pacific, August 1945. Two M3 machine guns are hung with gear at right.

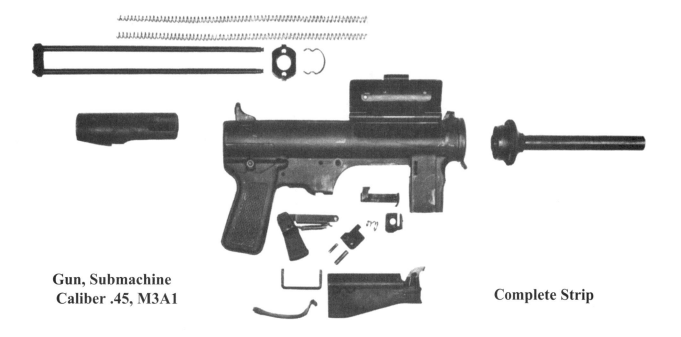

**Gun, Submachine
Caliber .45, M3A1**

Complete Strip

k. New undercuts on the bolt.
l. New safety lock.
m. Use of a conventional type extractor.

During the development stages of the M3E1 Submachine Gun the following changes and additions in characteristics were made:

a. Eliminate the use of a conventional type extractor.
b. Eliminate the ratchet assembly with an on-off type barrel lock and utilizing the previously approved ratchet assembly
c. Locate ejector in housing instead of receiver.
d. Incorporate an ejector slot cut the full length of the bolt as well as a cut through the guide rod retaining plate to permit removal of barrel assembly without necessitating the removal of the housing.
e. Redesign the stock to permit its use as a magazine loader, thus eliminating the requirement for a separate item for this purpose, plus drilling and tapping forward ends to accommodate a cleaning brush.
f. Incorporate a stronger rear sight wherein strengthening webs were to be added to both sides of the "L" type sight previously used. (This design of sight, and the above mentioned stock were authorized for inclusion in production of the M3 Submachine Gun.)

Six pilot models of the M3E1 Submachine Gun were completed and two were transmitted to the Infantry Board, Fort Benning, Georgia, for informative tests, and two were demonstrated at Aberdeen Proving Ground.

Since none of the changes incorporated in the M3E1 Submachine Gun had any adverse affect upon the reliability of functioning of the weapon, no formal program of test was carried out, but sufficient firings were conducted to satisfy interested personnel as to the desirability of the changes incorporated. In December 1944 the M3E1 Submachine Gun was adopted as Gun, Submachine, Caliber .45, M3A1, thus reclassifying the M3 as Limited Standard.

In April 1945 approval was granted for the replacement of the Thompson Submachine Guns, Caliber .45, M1928A1, M1, and M1A1, with the M3 and M3A1 Submachine Guns. The Thompson type submachine guns withdrawn from service were to be used for international purposes.

The M3A1 Submachine Gun, like its predecessor the M3, is all metal, fabricated mainly of stamped parts to take advantage of speed and economy of manufacture and assembly. Its weight distribution, with its low cyclic rate, allows unusual accuracy for a weapon of this type, whether used as a pistol, or with the stock extended. The working parts are fully enclosed to protect them against dirt, water, and mud. There are no projecting moving parts to endanger the operator. The receiver assembly is fabricated from

Gun Submachine, Caliber .45, M3A1

(1) Finger Hole
(2) Larger Ejection Port
(3) Disassembly Flats on
     Barrel Collar

two stamped symmetrical halves, welded together. The rear sight, barrel bushing, sear pin bushings, hinge assembly, and sling loops are all welded in place, and the cover, stock catch, and ratchet are added to complete the assembly. The pistol grip has incorporated therein a large capacity oil can, which is made as an assembly to the pistol grip. A cap on the bottom of the pistol grip has attached thereto a stylus, which serves the dual purpose of a means of oiling the gun, as well as of a drift to remove the extractor retaining pin.

The bolt featuring an integral firing pin, a semifixed spring type extractor, and a finger hole for cocking is designed to form a complete assembly with its guide rods and driving springs. Dual guide rods and springs are employed to furnish complete support and control independent to the receiver during the bolt travel. This gives accurate guiding, smoother operation, and uniformity of driving spring loading with a minimum of wear, dirt, and lubrication troubles. The assembly is easily removed for inspection, cleaning, or conversion.

A conventional integrated assembly is made of the sear, connector, trigger, and spring for ease in assembling and disassembling in the receiver.

The housing mounts the ejector, closes the opening in the bottom of the receiver, and retains all pins, the magazine catch, spring, and shield.

The stock is equipped with transverse bar to act as a stop when used as a cleaning rod to prevent injury to the barrel. This bar has a short stud incorporated which acts as a magazine follower depressor, thereby allowing the stock to serve as a magazine loader, eliminating the standard magazine loader accessory.

The cover assembly insures a closed, safe gun when not in use, and protects the interior against mud, rain, and dust. The integral safety lug on the cover locks the bolt forward when closed on an empty chamber, with loaded magazine in place, or retains the bolt as-

sembly with barrel removed for shipping. In the cocked position the safety lock cams the bolt back off the sear, making the sear and trigger inoperative.

An outstanding feature is the method in which the gun may be field stripped for cleaning. No tools of any sort are required.

GUN, SUBMACHINE
CALIBER .30, CARBINE

During the fall of 1944, it appeared desirable to investigate the possibility of modifying the design of the M3 Submachine Gun to permit the firing of the Carbine Cartridge Caliber .30, M1. This investigation was entered into in view of the many reports received from the field recommending the development of a submachine gun, which would fire the carbine caliber .30 round. Further information was received to the effect that the Germans were using the MP 43, 7.92 Machine Pistol, wherein a shortened 7.92-mm cartridge was used.

In the redesign of the M3 Submachine Gun to accomplish the above, it was necessary to use a spring loaded ejector in order to soften up ejection. Considerable study was given by personnel of the design section of Guide Lamp Division of General Motors Corporation to a proper balance of driving springs. In order to facilitate retracting the bolt and still maintain the proper spring load to prevent the bolt from striking the rear of the receiver in recoil, it was necessary to employ both a short, stronger spring and a longer, low rate spring — the short spring being required primarily to stop the bolt in recoil and the long spring to feed and fire the cartridge. Three modified M3 Submachine Guns designated as T29, incorporating the basic design characteristics of the M3A1 Submachine Gun were completed and function fired 1,500 rounds per gun.

Study of the T29 Submachine Gun showed that the type of spring loaded ejector, the type of feed ramp necessary, and the design of spring would require further development. However, in that the Carbine, Caliber .30, M2, selective semi- and full-automatic fire was standardized it was not deemed advisable to continue further development work on the T29 model.

A physical sample of this item and drawings pertaining thereto were retained at Springfield Armory for possible future reference.

SILENCERS FOR SUBMACHINE GUNS

In the early part of the recent war, studies and experiments to develop satisfactory equipment and training methods were under way at the Infantry Board, Fort Benning, Georgia, and the question of using silencers on snipers' rifles was being considered and was to be determined by these experiments.

The silencers developed were both bulky and heavy and in most cases utilized changeable rubber or felt washers and a series of baffles. Special ammunition, loaded to velocities under that of sound, were usually used in conjunction with the silencers. These types are exemplified by the German Silenced Machine Pistol "Pi Erma," a 7.9-mm carbine, and the British 9-mm Welgun.

The following list of "silenced" submachine guns and rifles were tested during the past 3 years at the Aberdeen Proving Ground and at the Infantry Board;

> Thompson Submachine, Cal. .45,
>   with silencer by Chrysler Corporation
> Hornet, Cal. 22
>   with silencer by Bell Laboratory
> Cal. .22 Long Rifle
>   with silencer by Bell Laboratory
> Cal. .30 Carbine
>   with silencer by Bell Laboratory
> M3 Submachine Gun
>   with silencer by Bell Laboratory

"Our Platoon in Haller, Luxembourg. Ten of them are still with us. Dec. 27th '44". Thirty-four men are visible in this picture taken during the Battle of the Bulge. The two arms at center right are M-3 submachine guns. At right is a BAR, the remainder M1 Garands.

The object of the test of these weapons equipped with silencers was to ascertain whether detection of position of the firer could be made by observers not knowing from which location the gun was fired.

In the Aberdeen tests, gunners fired single rounds from the various weapons, from variable positions on the firing front, the observers being placed at 100, 200, and 300 yards from the gunners. These tests resulted in the following conclusions: the silent weapons were located by observers as easily as unsilenced weapons; all silencers gave considerable noise reduction and that silencers tested were too bulky for practical military application.

The Office of Strategic Services tested the M3 Submachine Gun with the Bell Laboratory design of silencer and requested that the Ordnance Department furnish 1,000 special barrels for use with "silenced" M3 Submachine Guns.

The 1,000 silenced barrels were fabricated by Guide Lamp Division of General Motors Corporation and transmitted, by direction of Office, Strategic

**M3 Submachine Gun
with Silencer by Bell Laboratory**

Services, to the Hi-Standard Manufacturing Company, who assembled the silencer components to the barrel.

Although this item was tested by the Infantry Board, no further requirement other than the above was established.

Library of Congress
LC-G612-T-43524

**Indoor range at the Naval Training Facility, Bainbridge, Maryland — 1944.
M2 Springfield rifles are being used in the foreground.**

Naval Historical Center

**"3-42 - Virgin Island Home Guards being instructed by Marines on .22 cal. range."
All the rifles visible are M2 Springfield .22 Caliber rifles.**

U.S. Rifle, Caliber .22, M1922

Obsolete by World War II it led to the improved M1 and M2 U.S. Training Rifles and spurred the development of match quality commercial .22 caliber rifles.

.22 CALIBER TRAINING RIFLES

The gallery practice rifle developed prior to World War I on the design of Majors J.E. Hoffer and J.T. Thompson utilized a .22 caliber barrel mounted on a standard production 1903 Rifle, combined with the use of steel caliber .22 short cartridge holders machined in the form of the 1906 .30 caliber cartridge. The barrel was chambered with a shorter chamber to preclude chambering of the standard .30 caliber cartridge. The receiver bridge was also stamped "22". This arm could utilize the standard 5-round clip. It was found in practice that the cartridge holders would become damaged at their muzzle end when they fell to the ground in firing practice. There was also a problem of corrosion of both the cartridge holders and the barrel due to the chlorate primers used. Due to the demands for the 1903 rifle during World War I, decision was made to purchase from the Winchester Co. a large quantity of Winder Muskets, a falling block .22 Short Caliber arm. Both the Hoffer Thompson designed 1903 .22 caliber rifle and the Winder Musket would be withdrawn from service after World War I, the standard issue Model 1903 Rifle using the Cartridge, Gallery Practice, Caliber .30 M1919 being preferred for indoor gallery practice.

The new caliber .22 pattern of U.S. rifle was initially developed by the Ordnance Department with the assistance of the National Rifle Association, to provide an accurate small-bore weapon for use of civilian rifle clubs, for use in rifle competitions in schools and colleges, and for sales purpose to members of the National Rifle Association. Subsequently, the weapon was adopted for use in small-bore rifle marksmanship courses throughout the Army, Navy, Marine Corps, and Coast Guard. The rifles assembled for use of rifle clubs have the NRA type of stocks and butt plates (shotgun type), while those assembled for military use have the military type of stocks and butt plates.

U.S. RIFLE, CALIBER .22, M1922

As initially produced, this rifle was designated as Rifle, U.S., caliber .22, M1922. Successive improvements have been indicated by the designations M1922MI (later changed to M1) and M2. In general, these changes in designation were caused by major improvements in the bolt and firing mechanism, and may be applied to any model. The original design of this rifle contained the M1922 Bolt Assembly, which included a double-point striker and headed cocking piece, the M1922 Magazine Assembly, which projected below the floor plate, and a No. 48B Lyman receiver sight. This sight has five graduations to one complete revolution of the elevating and windage screw knobs. Most of these rifles were assembled with the NRA type of stock (stock, M1922, assembly) and shotgun type of butt plate (plate, butt, M1922). Nearly all these rifles now have later type bolts and magazines, and the sights have been changed to the No. 48C Lyman receiver sight in general use on subsequent models.

U.S. RIFLE, CALIBER .22, M1

This rifle, formerly designated as the M1922MI, was the result of the first improvement to the M1922 Rifle, and included the bolt with the M1 Firing Mechanism Assembly, the M1 Magazine Assembly, and the No. 48C Lyman receiver sight. The improved bolt permitted more accurate headspace adjustment, which is critical in such small-bore weapons. The new magazine was made to set flush with the floor plate, and the new sight provided 10 graduations to one complete revolution of the elevating and windage screws. All these improvements may and probably have been applied to all M1922 Rifles except those sold to individuals.

Springfield M1 .22 Caliber Rifle

NOTE: U.S. Rifle, Cal. .22, M1922MI (NRA) is identical with the regular M1922MI Rifle in so far as markings are concerned, but is assembled to the M1922 Stock Assembly D1823, which takes the M1922 Butt Plate. As already stated, the original designation of M1922MI was changed to M1.

U.S. RIFLE, CALIBER .22, M2

The M2 rifle is the result of the second improvement of the original M1922 rifle. The improvements were made in two stages:

The first stage included a redesigned bolt with firing mechanism assembly, magazine assembly, and stock assembly, which were designated as M2. Approximately 3,800 rifles were so assembled.

The second stage was a redesign of the bolt handle to incorporate an adjustable headspace feature, composed of a headspace adjusting screw and set screw. In addition, the fall of the firing pin was reduced to one-half that of the previous model, and the bolt head and magazine were modified to permit the uppermost cartridge to be in line with the chamber, thus reducing feed jams.

NOTE: Bolt handles of the first-stage design were replaced with the redesigned bolt handles containing the adjustable headspace feature as the rifles containing them were turned in for overhaul.

A later modification of the bolt handle with adjustable head space feature slightly modified the bolt handle and head space adjusting screw, and substituted a copper locking plug for the set screw. Both adjusting screw and locking plug were sealed in place after adjustment.

A still later modification of the bolt handle group changed the head space adjusting screw from one with a slotted head to one with an "Allen" set screw type of head, and eliminated the sealing of the screw and locking plug after adjustment. The M2 Bolt (with firing mechanism, assembly) and M2 Magazine Assembly may be used together in the M1922 and MI Rifles. When so used, regardless of type of stock, the rifles will be marked as follows:

RIFLE, U.S. cal. .22, M1922M2 (adding "M2" to original marking)

RIFLE, U.S. cal. .22, MII (adding "I" to original marking)

In addition to above marking, there will also be added to serial numbers of the converted M1922 and M1 Rifles the letters "A" and "B" respectively.

NOTE: Rifles originally stamped as M1922MI will have marking M1922MII, and the letter "B" after the serial number when so converted.

The No. 48B and C Lyman receiver sights are practically identical with parts of the C-sight replaced as was needed for either the B- or C-sight.

Springfield M2 .22 Caliber Rifle

Remington 513T .22 Caliber Rifle

COMMERCIAL RIFLES

With the decision made by 1939 to concentrate production at Springfield Armory on the Rifle .30 Caliber, M1 cessation of M1903A1 rifle production was made in 1939 - the bulk of the M1903A1 machinery was shipped to Rock Island in 1940. Likewise new production on Rifles, Caliber .22 M2 was to be brought to a halt, this however not being accomplished until 1942 in which year over 3000 M2 Rifles were assembled. In late 1940 the decision was made, as in World War I, to rely upon commercial sources for .22 caliber training rifles. In addition to allowing increased concentration of effort on the M1 service rifle, there was the added advantage of greatly lowering the acquisition cost of .22 caliber training rifles.

The commercial rifles, Remington Model 513T, Stevens Model 416-2, Winchester Model 75 and Mossberg Model 44 US are basically the same as the M1 and M2 Rifles. All are of bolt action type, have five to seven round magazines, have sling swivels and are equipped with rear sights adjustable for windage and elevation. Front sights are of the blade type, except for the Stevens, which may have a blade or hooded type with five inserts. The weights of these rifles approximate the weight of the M1 .30 caliber service rifle - all four rifles being between 7.9 and 8.9 pounds. In total over 200,000 commercial .22 caliber rifles were procured during World War II.

Remington 513T .22 Caliber Rifle

Remington Arms Company of Ilion, New York supplied approximately 70,000 Model 513T rifles, which had the following features:

Weight:	8.20 lbs
Length:	45.0 in.
Barrel Length:	27.0 in.
Number of grooves:	6
Twist:	1 Turn in 16 in.
Rear Sight:	Redfield 75-RT
Trigger pull	4 to 6 lbs.
Adjustable pull	Yes
Sight radius	33.4 in.

Stevens 416-2 .22 Caliber Rifle

J. Stevens Arms Company of Chicopee Falls, Massachusetts supplied approximately 10,000 Model 416-2 rifles, which had the following features:

Weight:	8.70 lbs
Length:	45.8 in.
Barrel Length:	26.1 in.
Number of grooves:	6
Twist:	1 Turn in 16 in.
Rear Sight:	Stevens
Trigger pull	4 to 6 lbs.
Adjustable pull	No
Sight radius	32.8 in.

Stevens 416-2 .22 Caliber Rifle

Winchester Model 75 .22 Caliber Rifle

Winchester Model 75 .22 Caliber Rifle

Winchester Repeating Arms Company of New Haven, Connecticut supplied approximately 17,000 Model 75 rifles, which had the following features:

Weight:	7.90 lbs
Length:	45.0 in.
Barrel Length:	28.1 in.
Number of grooves:	6
Twist:	1 Turn in 16 in.
Rear Sight:	Lyman 57E
Trigger pull	4 to 6 lbs.
Adjustable pull	Yes
Sight radius	32.8 in.

Mossberg 44 US .22 Caliber Rifle

O.F. Mossberg & Sons, Inc. of New Haven, Connecticut supplied approximately 60,000 Model 44 US rifles, which had the following features:

Weight:	8.50 lbs
Length:	43.3 in.
Barrel Length:	26.0 in.
Number of grooves:	6
Twist:	1 Turn in 16 in.
Rear Sight:	Lyman 57MS or Mossberg S-100
Trigger pull	4 to 6 lbs.
Adjustable pull	Yes
Sight radius	30.5 in.

The Remington Model 513T, Stevens Model 416-2, and the Winchester Model 75 commercial rifles had been approved as substitute standard in late 1940 as part of the war mobilization effort to allow concentration of effort by the Springfield Armory on the primary U.S. Service Rifle, the Rifle .30 Caliber M1. Direction was put out in 1941 to purchase all existing stocks of the Remington Model 513T, Stevens Model 416-2, Winchester Model 75 rifles in addition to contracts placed for these rifles. However, the three named firms supplying .22 caliber training rifles were also being called upon to produce service rifles - the .30 caliber M1 rifle at Winchester; the M1903, M1903A3 and M1903A4 rifles at Remington; and for our British allies under Lend-Lease agreements the Short Lee Enfield .303 rifle at the Stevens plant in Chicopee Falls, Massachusetts. This production, as well as other calls upon these firms for machine guns and small arms parts lead to the decision in late 1942 to adopt the Mossberg Model 44 US as a limited substitute. An earlier model, the Model 42 MB had been produced by the firm of O.F. Mossberg for Britain under Lend-Lease; however this arm was deemed of insufficient weight as a U.S. training rifle. It was redesigned to simplify production, weight was added to the barrel, and the stock modified to more closely resemble the heft and balance of the service rifle. The Mossberg 44 US was the result of this effort, it resembling closely the physical dimensions of the other commercial .22 caliber training rifles. It also has a plastic trigger guard and plate and a birch versus a walnut stock - both features conserving critical war production materials.

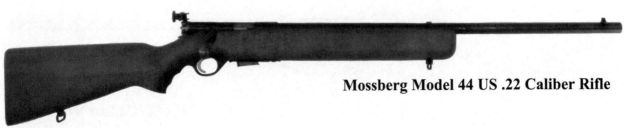

Mossberg Model 44 US .22 Caliber Rifle

Early production Model 44 US Rifles had a blued finish, later production arms are parkerized.

USMC .22 CALIBER TRAINING RIFLE

Harrington & Richardson Model 65
USMC Semi-Automatic .22 Caliber Rifle

Harrington & Richardson, Inc. of Worcester, Massachusetts supplied approximately 6,000 Model 65 rifles to the United States Marine Corps, which had the following features:

Weight:	8.80 lbs
Length:	43.0 in.
Barrel Length:	23.0 in.
Number of grooves:	6
Twist:	1 Turn in 16 in.
Rear Sight:	Redfield 70
Trigger pull	4 to 6 lbs.
Adjustable pull	No
Sight radius	28 in.
Magazine capacity	10 Rounds

The adoption of the Harrington & Richardson Model 65 semi-automatic .22 Caliber training rifle by the United States Marine Corps in late 1943 demonstrates, once again, the superiority of the firepower provided by the M1 Garand semi-automatic rifle adopted by the Army in January 1936. In 1940 the Marine Corps did not adopt the M1 semi-automatic rifle, instead retaining the Model 1903 Springfield bolt-action rifle through the early Pacific islands campaigns. However, the Guadalcanal campaign proved to the Marine soldier the M1's superiority in firepower as well as reliability. By 1943 the M1 had superceded the 1903 Rifle in the Marine Corps. Along with the use of the M1 Rifle the Marine Corps came to change its tactical doctrine and felt the need to introduce into their training program a semi-automatic .22 caliber training rifle designed to imitate the weight, balance, and firepower of the M1 service rifle. However, a properly designed .22 caliber semi-automatic rifle was not available.

Harrington & Richardson Model 65
USMC .22 Caliber Semi-automatic Rifle

Early production Model 65 Rifles had a blued finish, later production arms were parkerized.

The Navy Department had previously tested and purchased an estimated 20,000 Model 50 .45 caliber Harrington & Richardson Reising submachine guns for use by both the Navy and the Marine Corps. The Model 50 .45 caliber H&R Reising submachine gun was a delayed blowback arm designed by Eugene C. Reising. Harrington & Richardson had also submitted an experimental .30 caliber carbine in the 1941 carbine trials that had led to the adoption of the Winchester-designed M1 carbine. It was proposed to the Harrington & Richardson Company by the Marine Corps that a .22 caliber semiautomatic rifle be developed on a similar design. The task fell to Eugene C. Reising who designed the Model 65 .22 caliber semi-automatic rifle using a simple blowback design.

The H&R Model 65 .22 caliber semi-automatic rifle, of which 7,000 are believed to have been procured, incorporated several notable design features, especially the front sight, which duplicates the M1 Garand service rifle and M1 carbine front sight, with the two protective wings. Likewise, the weight of 8.8 pounds closely approximates the weight of the M1 rifle. This attention to detail is laudable from a training viewpoint. The operating bolt, however, is not in the same location as either the M1 rifle or M1 carbine, which are to the right, slightly above and behind the entrance to the chamber. On the H&R Reising Model 65 .22 caliber semiautomatic rifle the operating bolt is to be found immediately underneath the barrel, located in an opening in the stock. The metal parts are parkerized, the rear sight is adjustable for windage and elevation, though of a different design than either the M1 rifle or the M1 carbine.

The Harrington & Richardson Model 65 .22 caliber semi-automatic rifle is notable as being the first semi-automatic .22 caliber training rifle adopted by any of the service branches of the United States. Its adoption pays testimony of the superiority of the M1 Rifle and points to the future of .22 caliber training rifles.

"Okinawa. Marines of the 2nd Battalion 22nd Regiment land at Green Beach One." The lead Marine carries a M1 Thompson, the second Marine carries a M2-2 Flamethrower and a .45.

Back Row — Capt. John W. Scott, Lt. Donald D. Eachran, Unidentified, 1st Lt. Mortimer K. Smith. *Front Row* — Sgt. Otto Russell, Sgt. Ralph H. Thomas Jr., T/Sgt John J. Barry, Cpl. Homer G. Harper, T/Sgt. Rodney J. Edwards and Corporal Joel W. Griffin.

Crew of B-24 "Tailskid Tolly," 403rd Squadron, 43rd Bomb Group, 5th Air Force, June 15, 1943, Port Moresby, New Guinea. Note the .45 on waist belt at left, the rest wear shoulder holsters. They would crash eight days later in the "Taxpayers Pride," with only Cpl. Joel Griffin surviving.

Gunny Sgt. Roy L. Parker at his temporary residence in Okinawa cleaning his M1911 .45.

**Pistol, Automatic
Caliber .45, M1911A1**

**Manufactured by
Colt's Patent Firearms
Manufacturing Company**

Collection of Earl J. Coates

PISTOLS AND REVOLVERS

Since 1911 the U.S. Pistol, Automatic, Caliber .45, M1911 has been the standard side arm of our armed forces. Ever since the Civil War, American fighting men have held the handgun in high regard whenever they were faced with the problem of disposing of the enemy in personal combat.

The background of the Colt, Caliber .45 goes back through the years to 1892, when John Browning first began to experiment with the idea of making some of the muzzle blast following the discharge of a gun do the work of reloading it for another shot. The results of Browning's early experiments were brought to Colt about 1897. At first the idea was for a hammerless weapon that would fire full-automatic. In the next three years of development, the full-automatic feature was discarded as impossible to control in a one-handed gun, and the hammer was placed on the outside. This resulted in the Colt Automatic Pistol, Caliber .38, Model 1900. At that time the standard service side arm was the Colt New Army and New Navy .38 caliber double action revolver, which had taken the place of the old .45 single action Army, which had been in use since the early 1870's. The value of the .38 caliber revolver as a manstopper was beginning to be questioned because of its frequent failure to halt charging natives in the Philippines cam-

paign before they killed or wounded American troops.

This situation resulted in a joint series of tests in 1903 and 1904 by Ordnance Officers and the Army Medical Corps. The Board tested bullets all the way from a .30 Luger up to the British .476. As a result of these tests the Board decided that no bullet less than .45 caliber, or less than 230 grains weight was suitable for service pistol use.

PISTOL, CALIBER .45, M1905

The Model of 1905 Caliber .45 Military Automatic Pistol, similar in appearance to the .38, had no safely but was equipped with slide locks. This pistol, the Savage Automatic, and several foreign automatics, including Luger, Bergmann, Bayard, and Shoboue, in .45 caliber, were extensively tested in 1906 and 1907. As a result of these tests some changes were made in the Model M1905, Caliber .45, which included application to the pistol of a small grip safety and a better shaped spur hammer in place of the rounded hammer.

Field tests conducted between 1908 and 1910 indicated the need of a very thorough overhauling and refinement of the whole model and resulted in the Model M1911.

**Pistol, Automatic
Caliber .45, M1911**

Marines at the entrance to a Japanese dugout —
the center Marine holds a .45 Automatic pistol.
His comrades carry M1 Garand rifles. Photo was
taken on the Caroline Islands.

PISTOL, AUTOMATIC, CAL. .45, M1911

The Model M1911 Pistol was fitted with both grip and manual safeties and with a slide lock. This model, chambered for the original caliber .45 Colt cartridge, was adopted in 1911 as the standard service pistol.

During World War I the M1911 Pistol proved its superior usefulness in trench fighting, thus a decision was reached in mid 1917 to supply the infantry with a more extensive equipment of automatic pistols than had previously been prescribed by regulations—to build them by hundreds of thousands where we had been turning them out by thousands. In February 1917, with war in sight, realizing the limitations of our capacity then for producing pistols, the Colt automatic being manufactured exclusively by the Colt's Patent Firearms Manufacturing Co. at Hartford, Conn., and for a limited period by the Springfield Armory, the Ordnance Department took up with the Colt Co. the proposition of securing drawings and other engineering data, which would enable us to extend the production of this weapon to other plants. Production would be suspended at Springfield in April 1917 to devote full efforts to the production of rifles, with only 2,412 pistols being assembled in fiscal year 1917 - the remaining pistol components shipped to Colt Co. for completion. In December 1917, the Remington Arms-Union Metallic Cartridge Co. was instructed to prepare for the manufacture of 150,000 automatics, Colt model 1911, at a rate to reach a maximum production of 3,000 per day. Considerable difficulty was experienced in obtaining the necessary drawings and designs, because the manufacture of these pistols at the Colt Co. plant had been largely in the hands of expert veteran mechanics, who knew tricks of fitting and assembling not apparent in the drawings. During the summer of 1918 in order to fill the enormously increased pistol requirements

Standing — Novice, Co-Pilot; Lockhart; Jardine; Karper; Pyles.
Front row — Miller; Lawrence Million; Schlaegel; Null; Grilley.

Aircrewmen of the "Der Grossarchnogel," 613th Squadron, 401st Bomb Group, 8th Air Force, after their 7th mission to Montbartier, France in their B-17. A .45 is carried 2nd right, back row. The camaraderie of the bomber crews is evident. In this survey picture the donator ensured the names of crew were included. The contributing author's Uncle John L. Fox also flew with the 8th Air Force. He went down with the rest of his crew three times, in three planes, the 2nd the "Princess Pat", 3rd on 19th mission over Hamburg, ending up as POWs. Their camaraderie has lasted over 50 years.

"Marines cautiously probe a cave on Tinian 28 July 1944. Note that the lead man has a .45 pistol".

"Norman Rand forges frames for .45 caliber automatic pistols" at the Colt plant in Hartford.

"John Ignacek pierces trigger holes on .45 caliber automatic pistols" at Colt's factory.

Anthony Freda drills the frames of .45 caliber automatic pistols at the Colt plant in Hartford.

"Anna Healey turns and drills butt millings on ejector of .45 caliber automatic pistols".

Pawl being drilled on a belt driven drill press, whose design predates the Civil War.

William Watson gauges and inspects frames.

The photographs on this and the preceding page were photographed by Andreas Feininger in July 1942 at the Colt Manufacturing Company, in Hartford Connecticut for the Office of War Information.

"Under Guard. Marines guarding this Jap soldier are taking no chances as both of them keep drawn 45's on their man, while waiting for an interpreter to come to question him. July 9, 1944, Saipan." Photo by Sgt. R.B. Opper.

"The terror of the Japanese soldiers in the dugouts and pillboxes on Iwo Jima is the flamethrowing man. Briefly this one is outlined against the bleak sky as he rushes forward into position to assault a Jap pillbox on Motoyuma Airfield Number Two." He carries an M2-2 flame thrower and a holstered .45 Automatic.

of the American Expeditionary Forces, contracts for the Colt automatic were given to the National Cash Register Co., at Dayton, Ohio; the North American Arms Co., Quebec; the Savage Arms Co., Utica, N. Y.; Caron Bros., Montreal; the Burroughs Adding Machine Co., Detroit, Mich.; the Winchester Repeating Arms Co., New Haven, Conn.; the Lanston Monotype Co., Philadelphia, Pa.; and the Savage Munitions Co., San Diego, Calif. All of these concerns, none of which had ever before produced the .45-caliber pistol, were proceeding energetically with their preparations for manufacture when the armistice came to cancel their contracts. No pistols were ever obtained from any except the Colt's Patent Fire Arms Manufacturing Co. and the Remington Arms-Union Metallic Cartridge Co.

Difficulty was experienced in securing machinery to check the walnut grip for the pistols, and to avoid delay in production the Ordnance Department authorized the use of Bakelite for pistol grips in all the new plants, which were to manufacture the gun. Bakelite is a substitute for hard rubber or amber, invented by the eminent chemist Dr. Baekeland.

At the outbreak of World War I the Army owned approximately 75,000 Model 1911 .45-caliber automatic pistols. At the signing of the armistice there had been produced and accepted since April 6, 1917, a total of 643,755 pistols and revolvers. The production of pistols was 375,404 and that of revolvers 268,351. In the four months prior to November 11, 1918, the average daily production of automatic pistols was 1,993 and of revolvers 1,233. This was at the yearly production rate of approximately 600,000 pistols and 370,000 revolvers. These pistols were produced at an approximate cost of $15 each. Production of pistols and revolvers from April 1917 to Dec. 31, 1918 included 425,500 M1911 Pistols by Colt, and 13,152 by Remington U.M.C.

Pistol, Automatic Caliber .45, M1911

Manufactured at the Springfield Armory

**Pistol, Automatic
Caliber .45, M1911A1**

production demands placed upon that company, including revolvers and machine guns. The Ithaca Gun Co., manufacturer of shotguns before the war, was contracted in 1942 and would produce a third of a million pistols by war's end. The firm of Remington Rand, Inc., a producer of typewriters and office machinery before the conflict, would produce about a million pistols at a new factory utilizing new and more productive machinery allocated with the assistance of the War Production Board.

PISTOL, AUTOMATIC, CAL. .45, M1911A1

The Model 1911, Caliber .45 Pistol was further modified after the first World War by the addition of the longer grip safety spur and an arched main spring housing and by cutting away a portion of the receiver just back of the trigger on the left side to allow smoother trigger control.

This model was designated as U. S. Pistol, Automatic, Caliber .45, M1911A1. During the inter-war period appropriations were small and only 34,000 M1911A1 pistols were procured. The first 10,000 pistols with the new features were procured in 1924 - the designation 1911A1, however, not being approved until 1926. None were procured for the next dozen years, with procurements made in increasing quantities from 1937 onward until 14,000 were procured in the Fiscal Year ending June 1941. With the realization of the advent of war mobilization plans and contracts were initiated. Colt Manufacturing Co., the only existing manufacturer, would receive the first contracts, with the following orders going to the firms of Ithaca Gun Co., Inc. of Ithaca, New York; Remington Rand Inc., of Syracuse, New York; Union Switch & Signal Co. of Swissvale, Pennsylvania; and the Singer Manufacturing Co. of Elizabeth, New Jersey. The latter company would only receive a small educational contract, their production resources being deemed needed for other war efforts. Similarly the contracts given the Union Switch & Signal Co. would only total approximately 50,000 units, their production of railroad machinery and parts being deemed more important to the war effort. The vast bulk of the production would be made by three firms. The first contracted was Colt Co., who had first developed the arm and utilized their existing production facilities to produce over a half million M1911A1 pistols during the course of the war. This number would have been greater but for other pressing war

PISTOL SIGHTS

Pistols, M1911 and M1911A1, prior to 1942, were equipped with a rear sight having a shallow oval aperture and a smooth oval front sight. In April 1942, the corrugated front sight and the rear sight having a rectangular aperture were approved for incorporation in pistols in manufacture.

PISTOL, CALIBER .45, M1911 (DUMMY)

Six dummy Caliber .45, M1911 Pistols were submitted to the Office, Chief of Ordnance in November 1943, by the Cruver Manufacturing Company, Chicago, Illinois, with a view to the evaluation of their use as a training aid. This item is a dummy pistol, weighing the same as the standard M1911 Pistol, and it was thought that it might have some value in teaching trigger squeeze, sighting, and aiming, and familiarizing the student with the feel and balance of the standard model. Samples of this item were submitted to Headquarters, Army Ground Forces in January 1944 for examination and consideration as a training aid, and it was their decision that there was no requirement in Army Ground Forces for the item. It is believed the Navy procured a large quantity.

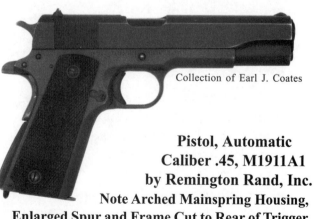

Collection of Earl J. Coates

**Pistol, Automatic
Caliber .45, M1911A1
by Remington Rand, Inc.**
**Note Arched Mainspring Housing,
Enlarged Spur and Frame Cut to Rear of Trigger**

"Corp. Ralph Cook, Troop. A. 112th Cav., covers a Jap under a log with his 45. The Jap was shot after resisting capture. Aitaps, New Guinea. 8/8/44" Photo by T/4 Stanley Lambert.

"Pfc. Lealon W. Brown of Hasca, Texas with flame-thrower and Pl. Sgt. Charles Koretzka, of Pittsburgh, Pa." Saipan, June 1944. Photo by Sgt. Bob Cooke. Pfc. Brown has drawn his .45 caliber automatic pistol.

"Private First Class Galen A. Brehm, 22, Fayette, Ohio, flame thrower for the Sixth Marine Division, plays a hot lick for the inhabitants of a cave on Okinawa". Marine Corps Doctrine called for flame thrower men to carry .45's. His holstered .45 is wrapped in plastic to protect it.

SPECIAL BARRELS FOR
PISTOL, CALIBER .45, M1911A1

In September 1943, a requirement was established by Headquarters, Army Air Forces for shot cartridges, caliber .45, for use in the M1911 and M1911A1 Pistols. Such cartridges were required for the purpose of killing small game to provide sustenance for Army Air Forces flying personnel forced down in uninhabited areas. During the development of these shot cartridges, the need for a special smoothbore shotgun type barrel to obtain adequate dense shot patterns became apparent; the rifling in the standard barrel produced excessive dispersion of shot.

Accordingly, a project was initiated to develop a special barrel for shot cartridges, and preferably one which would fire ball ammunition in emergencies. Several designs of barrels were fabricated by O.F. Mossberg and Sons, Inc., and submitted to the Aberdeen Proving Ground for test. These barrels included standard length smooth and cylinder bore, standard length with a short section of rifling at the throat; smooth bore with shotgun choke at muzzle; standard length with rifled breech and recess choke muzzle,

and a special 8-inch rifled barrel. Results of test indicated that a longer barrel would be more satisfactory. Consequently unrifled barrels of 10-, 12-, 14-, and 18-inch length were secured, each length represented by both choke and cylinder bore samples.

Tests at the Ordnance Research Center, Aberdeen Proving Ground, Maryland, indicated that all of these barrels, in both types of boring, produced satisfactory shot patterns. At a range of 25 feet, approximately 92 percent of the shot pellets struck in a 20-inch circle, and 96 percent in a 30-inch circle. Included in this test was a cylinder bore barrel extension, which could be attached by means of a modified barrel bushing. Shot patterns from this item were fairly satisfactory, but mechanically the means of attachment was poor, resulting in breakage of the barrel bushing on the tenth round fired.

The above barrels were service tested by Army Air Forces Board and resulted in the adoption of the 10-inch cylinder bore barrel for use in the Pistol, Automatic. Caliber .45, M1911 and M1911A1 for the purpose of issue to Army Air Forces personnel. This barrel was adopted in September 1945, and was designated as Barrel, Smooth Bore C7162249.

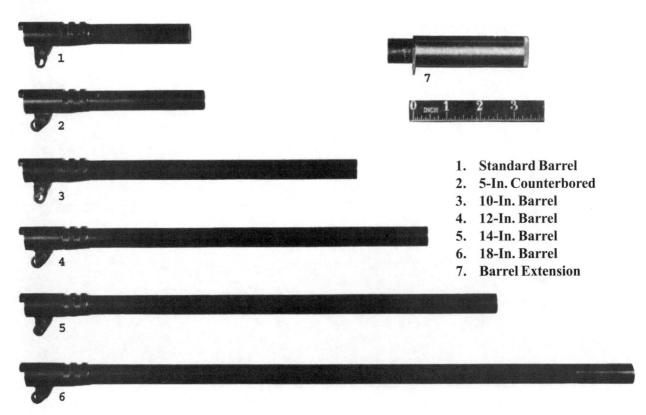

1. **Standard Barrel**
2. **5-In. Counterbored**
3. **10-In. Barrel**
4. **12-In. Barrel**
5. **14-In. Barrel**
6. **18-In. Barrel**
7. **Barrel Extension**

Special Barrel for Use in Pistol, Automatic, Caliber .45, M1911A1
with Cartridge, Shot, Caliber .45, M15.

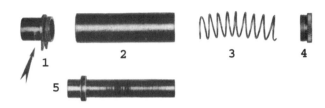

**Barrel Extension
for Use in Pistol, Automatic,
Caliber .45, M1911A1
With
Cartridge, Shot, Caliber .45, M15
Disassembled
(Note Lug Sheared Off)**

1. **Bushing**
2. **Sleeve**
3. **Spring**
4. **Collar**
5. **Barrel Extension**

Pvt. Dayton Lassiter MP in the 9th Infantry Division carries a Colt Model 1917 revolver, at the Belgian border — 12/11/1944.

**Revolver, Caliber .45,
Smith & Wesson, M1917**

REVOLVERS.

The Automatic Pistols, Caliber.45, M1911 and M1911A1, fulfilled the requirements of the armed services, other than the Military Police who preferred the M1917, Caliber .45, Revolver, Colt, or Smith & Wesson.

In May 1945, authority was requested and granted to discontinue repair of the M1917 Revolvers because there was no requirement for them. It was deemed advisable to effect obsoletion of this item in view of the quantity of pistols available, thus simplifying problems of supply and maintenance in the field as well as eliminating the necessity for manufacturing a new supply of repair parts. Reclassification of this item to obsolete was not concurred in by the Provost Marshall General, since it was considered a satisfactory weapon for police work, and it was found that should unforeseen demands arise, pistols or revolvers would be difficult to obtain for Military Police within the Continental United States.

The M1917 Colt and Smith & Wesson .45 Caliber Revolvers were produced during World War I in order to supplement the pistol supply. Although the Colt automatic was the only weapon of this sort approved for the Army, the Secretary of War authorized the Chief of Ordnance to secure other small arms, particularly the double-action .45-caliber revolver as manufactured by both the Colt Co. and the Smith & Wesson Co. These revolvers had been designed to use the standard Army caliber-.45 pistol cartridges loaded with two 3-round sheet metal clips.

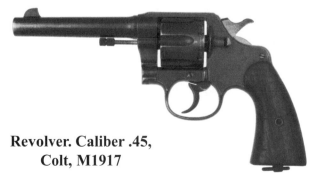

**Revolver. Caliber .45,
Colt, M1917**

127

**Colt, Caliber .45
Model 1917 Revolver**

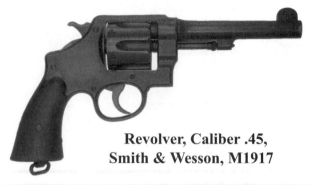

**Revolver, Caliber .45,
Smith & Wesson, M1917**

The revolver was not so effective a weapon as the automatic pistol, but it was adopted in the emergency only to make it possible to provide sufficient of these arms for the troops at the outset. At the start of hostilities the Colt Co. indicated that it could tool up to produce pistols at the rate of 6,000 per month by December 1917, and could also furnish 600 revolvers a week beginning in April. As soon as funds were available a contract was let with Colt for 500,000 pistols and 100,000 revolvers, and to the Smith & Wesson Co. for 100,000 revolvers. Although these contracts were not placed until June 15, 1917 in the certainty that funds would eventually be available both concerns had been working on the production of weapons on these expected contracts for many weeks. When in WWI orders came from France to increase the pistols an additional contract (P-5867-1431SA) for 172,000 1917 revolvers was awarded to Smith & Wesson on 18 May 1918 with 63,634 eventually de-livered through January 1919. Likewise Colt would receive an additional contract (P-4813-1368SA) for 206,000 revolvers - but this was terminated in December 1918. Colt would deliver to the Army a total of 154,802 Model 1917 revolvers.

There would be no Model 1917 revolvers contracted for or delivered during World War II.

National Archives

**"Crew of flame thrower tank Nobby on Saipan"
Pfc. Alfred L. Ickler with S&W 1917 revolver.
Cpl. William H. Sutley carries a M1 Thompson.**

Library of Congress
LC-USZ62-98986

"Crew members of a Marine torpedo bomber squadron lugging their own bags across the Okinawa airstrip as they arrive to start operations against the enemy." Photo by Corp. William Beall. The Marine Aviators have revolvers — probably .38s — in shoulder holsters.

Marine Corps Historical Center

Marines on Guadalcanal putting out a fire on a F4F Wildcat from a Japanese bomb. The Marine at left carries a holstered .45 automatic — the 2nd left Marine carries a revolver (probably a pilots .38 S&W) and has either an aviators cartridge loop belt or a western style belt with cartridge loops.

**Smith & Wesson
Revolver No. 85786
Chambered For Cartridge
Caliber .30 Carbine**

SMITH & WESSON REVOLVER CHAMBERED FOR CALIBER .30, CARBINE CARTRIDGE

The Smith & Wesson Company developed a revolver to fire the carbine cartridge and submitted this weapon to the Ordnance Department for test in January 1944. The weapon weighed 42 ounces, unloaded.

In tests at Aberdeen Proving Ground, a total of 1,232 rounds were fired with no malfunctions or breakages. The instrumental velocity obtained at 53 feet averaged 1,277 feet per second. A mean radius of 1.39 inches with an extreme spread of 4.18 inches was obtained by firing 10 targets of 10 shots each, at 25-yard range, by a shooter using two hands, on a sand bag rest. The muzzle blast was very sharp and caused considerable discomfort to the shooters without ear plugs.

Naval Historical Center

"US Army troops march captured German prisoners of war through Cherbourg, after the city's liberation 28 June 1944." The lead officers carry a M1 Carbine at left and pistol at right.

Oct 1943   Naval Historical Center

Ens. Frederick J. Joyce, USS Yorktown, CV10 beside his SBD. He carries a .38 S&W revolver.

Naval Historical Center

Marine Torpedo Bombing Squadron 232 and their scoreboard. .45s on left & .38 on right.

**Smith & Wesson
Revolver, Caliber .38**

SECONDARY PISTOLS & REVOLVERS

While the standard handgun was the .45 caliber M1911A1 there were procurements of a large quantity of other smaller caliber handguns during the war. These procurements may be categorized as follows:

1. Defense Supplies Corporation - revolvers for plant guard and police requirements.
2. Department of the Navy - revolvers for guard duty and aviators.
3. Lend Lease – handguns for our allies, primarily revolvers for Great Britain and the British Commonwealth.
4. .380 Colt semi-automatic pistols for General Officers.
5. .22 Caliber semi-automatic pistols for Navy training purposes.
6. Office of Strategic Services – silenced arms, and thousands of miscellaneous arms, including the Liberator, for resistance forces.

DEFENSE SUPPLIES CORPORATION .38 CALIBER REVOLVERS

Formed in 1940 for the war mobilization effort the Defense Supplies Corporation, a Federal Agency, purchased at least 130,000 revolvers. These procurements included purchases of revolvers from manufacturers, dealers, and wholesalers, including inventory, which had been frozen once the war had begun. The bulk of the procurements were for .38 caliber revolvers of the Smith & Wesson Military & Police, the Colt Official Police, and Colt Commando designs. These revolvers were supplied, at cost, to defense plants for guards, other Federal Agencies, and state and local police organizations.

NAVY .38 CALIBER REVOLVERS

Prior to the outbreak of the war the Navy Department in 1941 had contracted with the Smith & Wesson Company for 3000 .38 Special Military & Police revolvers for the U.S. Naval Civilian Police Corps. This contract would be followed during the war by contracts, initially by the Navy, then under the Army Ordnance department for over 300,000 .38 Special Smith & Wesson Military & Police revolvers (known as the Victory Model – the serial number is proceeded by the letter "V".) These revolvers were issued for guard duty, and, notably, were issued to Naval Aviators who utilized a Navy designed shoulder holster. It was reported that the Naval Aviators preferred the lighter and smaller .38 caliber revolvers in the tight confines of the aircraft cabin. Due to the accidental death of a sailor who dropped his sidearm, the Navy requested a change in the hammer block system of the Smith & Wesson revolver, which was accomplished in early 1945.

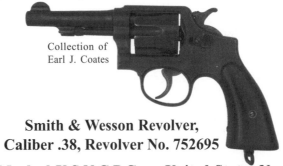

Collection of
Earl J. Coates

**Smith & Wesson Revolver,
Caliber .38, Revolver No. 752695**

Marked U.S.N.C.P.C. — United States Naval Civilian Police Corps. Received on 29 October 1941 at Bethlehem Steel at Sparrows Point, Baltimore, Maryland for Guard Duty.

Naval Historical Center

"Coast Guardsmen maintain constant vigil," here with a .38 Smith & Wesson Victory revolver.

Naval Historical Center

COMPOSITE SQUADRON NINETY-SIX – AIRCREWMEN

Left to Right –
FIRST ROW: S.J.Frederick,ARM3c; U.S.Wilson,ARM2c; L.B.Christensen,ARM2c; J.Arellano,ARM1c; R.Ballew,ARM3c;
             D.S.Craveiro,AMM2c; O.C.Wilfong,ARM2c; W.W.Larwood,ARM3c; E.P.Bradley,ARM3c; C.D.Wood,ARM2c;
SECOND ROW: M.M.Hendrickson,AOM3c; H.J.Gericke,AOM2c; T.F.Walsh,ARM3c; I.E.Thomas,ARM2c; W.O.Conger,ARM3c;
             G.C.Lanza,AOM1c; K.K.Myers,ARM3c; C.F.Albert,AMM2c; W.E.Adam,ARM3c; H.W.Snyder,AMM2c;
             G.S.Jefferies,AOM3c;
THIRD ROW: H.C.Mathey,ARM3c; C.K.King,ARM3c; G.H.Kaylor,ARM3c; W.R.Plinz,AMM2c; G.A.Anderson,AMM2c;
             J.G.Clark,ARM2c; D.E.Oswald,ARM2c; J.E.Benham,AOM3c; W.L.Graham,AOM3c; P.W.Hodges,ARM3c;
             J.D.Marshall,ARM3c; F.J.Bucinell,AMM3c;   MISSING – – H.E.Martin,AOM2c.

"Aircrewmen of Composite Squadron Ninety-Six (VC-96) photographed aboard USS Rudyerd Bay (CVE-81) on 24 April 1945". They carry holstered .38 revolvers and bandoliers — left center as a belt.

Naval Historical Center

.38 caliber — based on small grip size

"Great Lakes Naval Training Station, Ill. Revolver training at the service school for Negro Shore Patrolmen, November 1943. Guns are all Smith & Wesson revolvers"

Naval Historical Center

"USS Louisville (CA-28) SOC Pilot Ens. William C. Orr, USNR, and crewman, ARM3c Thomas D. Everett, pose by the damaged wingtip of their aircraft which was damaged by enemy fire." 26 February 1945. Orr carries a .38 S&W Revolver.

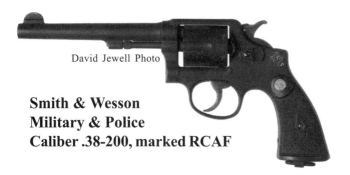

David Jewell Photo

**Smith & Wesson
Military & Police
Caliber .38-200, marked RCAF**

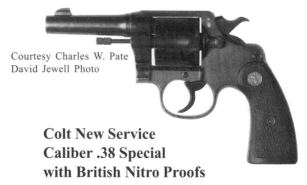

Courtesy Charles W. Pate
David Jewell Photo

**Colt New Service
Caliber .38 Special
with British Nitro Proofs**

ALLIED & LEND LEASE PROCUREMENTS, PRIMARILY .38 CALIBER REVOLVERS

Prior to the U.S. entry into the war, the British Government sent to the U.S. their Purchasing Commissions with a view to procure stocks of weapons to make up for their losses in the initial campaign successes of the Nazi aggressors and the shortfall of small arms caused by the lack of a large domestic firearms industry caused by their restrictive firearms laws. By the time of the U.S. entry into the war the British Purchasing Commissions had purchased over 250,000 Smith & Wesson Military & Police revolvers using both .38 Special and British .38-200 cartridges. After the U.S. entry into the war, Lend-Lease shipments of Smith & Wesson .38-200 Military & Police revolvers totaled over two thirds of a million to England and Canada.

The British Purchasing Commission also favored the Colt Patent Firearms Manufacturing Co. with purchases of approximately 50,000 Official Police .38-200 revolvers, along with smaller quantities of Colt handguns ranging in models from the .45 automatic to very small quantities of the obsolete single action army and in caliber from the Single Action's obsolete .45 Long Colt to .22 caliber Police Positive Target pistols. There was also a notable purchase of over 20,000 Harrington & Richardson Bobby .32 caliber revolvers used to arm the formerly unarmed British police.

Library of Congress
LC-USE6-D-009962

Smith & Wesson Lend Lease Revolvers being unpacked and recorded in Britain.

Library of Congress
LC-USE6-D-006252

"Angela Cherubini...machines bolt holes on the cylinder of .38 caliber revolvers" at Colt's.

Naval Historical Center

LtJG Ira J. Kepford of Fighter Squadron 17 beside his F4U-1A Corsair, with a .45 on 26 March, 1944.

Courtesy Charles W. Pate
West Point Museum
Serial # 135171

**Colt Pocket Model 1908
Caliber .380 Semi-Automatic
issued to General Eisenhower.**

GENERAL OFFICER'S .380
SEMI-AUTOMATIC PISTOLS

The Headquarters Army Service Forces approved procurement of 1,500 Pistols, automatic, caliber .380 on 11 August 1944 for issue to Army and Army Air Force General Officers by authority of "Instructions from Office, Chief of Staff, United States Army." The firm of Colt's Patent Fire Arms Manufacturing Company would supply their pocket model of 1908 hammerless pistols in caliber .380 automatic to fulfill this requirement and 1,000 in 1944 for Navy requisition ORD-01207. Notable issues of this pistol were numbers 135170 to General Patton and 135171 issued to General Eisenhower now in the West Point Museum.

Air Force Historical Research Agency

Major Charles W. Sweeney, Pilot.
509th Composite Group,
313th Bombardment Wing,
20th Air Force,
9 August 1945

"Major Sweeney checks out aircraft "Bock's Car" before takeoff on mission to Nagasaki." He carries a .45 on the second atomic mission.

USAMHI

Lt. Gen. L.K. Truscott wearing a Colt 1908 congratulates 1st Lt. J. W. Wells of the 442nd Japanese-American Combat Team.

David Jewell Photo
Courtesy Charles W. Pate
U.S. Handguns of World War II

**Colt Service Ace .22 Caliber
Semi-Automatic Pistol**

NAVY .22 CALIBER TRAINING PISTOLS

The procurement of Caliber .22 pistols was almost entirely to meet U.S. Navy requirements. The Department of the Navy desired the Colt Service Ace, with the "Carbine" Williams designed Floating Chamber, to be used as a training weapon due to its similarity to Colt M1911A1. However, due to the requirements for the caliber .45 M1911A1 pistols being produced by Colt, the Service Ace Pistol (which uses many components interchangeable with the M1911A1 caliber .45 pistol) could not be produced without reducing production of the .45 combat

Oahu 1943   Naval Historical Center

Admiral Chester W. Nimitz, Commander of the Pacific Fleet, firing a Colt Ace. Note the rear sight and reduced recoil of front of barrel. He had led the Pacific Fleet to Victory at Midway.

Naval Historical Center

"Waves at Treasure Island Naval Base, Ca., try their marksmanship with pistols during their training program. 11 Feb 1943". They are holding High Standard Model B .22 caliber pistols.

David Jewell Photo
Courtesy Charles W. Pate
U.S. Handguns of World War II

**Hi-Standard Model "B"
.22 Caliber Semi-Automatic Pistol**

weapon. As a result, the Navy agreed to accept High Standard .22 caliber pistols — approximately 14,000 Model "B" and 32,000 Model HD. Also accepted were 4,000 Colt Woodsman, regular and Match Target model

David Jewell Photo
Courtesy Charles W. Pate
U.S. Handguns of World War II

**Hi-Standard Model "HD"
.22 Caliber Semi-Automatic Pistol
approximating the M1911 in grip & weight.**

.22 caliber pistols. By 1945 reductions in requirements for the caliber .45 pistol enabled the Army Ordnance Department (who acted as contract agency for the
the Navy) to place a contract with Colt for 13,500 Service Ace .22 caliber pistols, of which two thirds were delivered before the end of the war.

David Jewell Photo
Courtesy Charles W. Pate
U.S. Handguns of World War II

**Colt Woodsman
.22 Caliber Semi-Automatic Pistol**

OFFICE OF STRATEGIC SERVICES – SILENCED ARMS

In the early part of World War II, studies and experiments to develop satisfactory equipment and training methods were under way at the Infantry Board, Fort Benning, Georgia, and the question of using silencers was to be determined by these experiments.

The silencers developed were both bulky and heavy and in most cases utilized special ammunition used in conjunction with the silencers. These types are exemplified by the German Silenced Machine Pistol "Pi Erma" and the British 9-mm Welgun.

The object of the test of these weapons equipped with silencers was to ascertain whether detection of position of the firer could be made by observers not knowing from which location the gun was fired.

In the Aberdeen tests, gunners fired single rounds from the various weapons, from variable positions on the firing front, the observers being placed at 100, 200, and 300 yards from the gunners. These tests resulted in the following conclusions; the silent weapons were located by observers as easily as unsilenced weapons; all silencers gave considerable noise reduction; and that silencers tested were too bulky for practical military application. The conclusion resulting from an Infantry Board test of a Caliber .22. Hi-Standard Pistol with silencer was that there was no infantry requirement for the subject pistol.

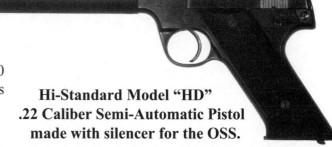

**Hi-Standard Model "HD"
.22 Caliber Semi-Automatic Pistol
made with silencer for the OSS.**

The Office of Strategic Services, however, found use for such an arm and utilizing a Bell Laboratory design contracted with the High Standard Manufacturing Company for over 2,000 silencer equipped Model H-D .22 caliber semi-automatic pistols during the war. The arm was to be used for close range sniping at sentries with its 90% reduction in noise – the remaining noise was primarily caused by metal contacts in the operation of the arm.

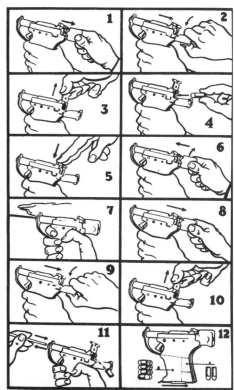

The Liberator, also the name of an Anti-Slavery Newspaper. As with John Brown's Pikes, the enslaved expected better weaponry from their allies.

Instruction sheet for the .45 Caliber "Flare Projector"

"FLARE PROJECTOR"
.45 CALIBER, SINGLE SHOT PISTOL

The Office of Strategic Services contracted with General Motor's Guide Lamp Division to produce a million .45 caliber single shot pistols. These were designed to be parachuted into enemy held territory in large numbers to be used at close quarters to obtain a better arm from an enemy soldier. The arm was produced primarily with stampings with minimal features - the barrel is unrifled and it lacks a cartridge extractor, which contributed to its low cost of under $2.00 each. The resistance forces, however, preferred the submachine gun.

US Army Military History Institute

"American soldiers of the 329th Regiment, 83rd Division string communications wire over a German Mark VI Tiger tank knocked out in the battle for Humelin, Belgium. 28 Dec 1944". The soldiers on left and right carry holstered .45 automatics.

National Archives

"4th Division artist Sgt. Fabion and Lt. J. P. Young, Jr., with Thompson sub-machine gun, moving up the ridge behind the tanks. June 1944, Saipan." Photograph by Hios. Sgt. Fabion carries a Model 1897 Winchester "Trench" shotgun. Combat use of the shotgun was common in the Marine Corps. The Thompson Lt. Young carries is a Model 1928A1.

"Shotguns mounted like machine guns, at skeet range, ground school near Lake Cabot, Calif."

Probably a Remington Model 11   Probably a Remington Model 31 Pump

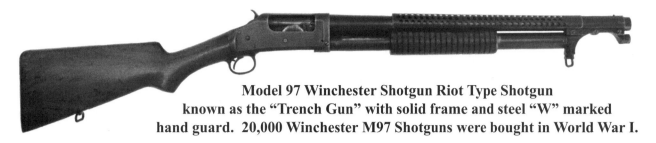

**Model 97 Winchester Shotgun Riot Type Shotgun
known as the "Trench Gun" with solid frame and steel "W" marked
hand guard. 20,000 Winchester M97 Shotguns were bought in World War I.**

SHOTGUNS

Classified as commercial standard shotguns in 1941 were the 12-gauge Remington, M10, the 12-gauge Winchester, M1897, Riot-type, and the 12-gauge Winchester, M1897, Sporting-type, or its commercial equal.

Because the Remington and Winchester firms were occupied with defense contracts in 1941, it was desirable to increase the number of possible sources of supply for weapons of this type. The manufacture of Remington M10 Shotguns had been discontinued about 1928. The Winchester M1897 was still made, but was commercially obsolescent.

As a result of these conditions the following models of shotguns were classified as commercial standard in August 1941:

Remington, M31
Winchester, M12
Ithaca, M37
Stevens, M620

These models were to be procured with 30-inch full choke sporting-type barrels for trap shooting purposes, 26 inch barrels for skeet shooting, and with 20 inch cylinder bore barrels equipped with sling swivels and a suitable attachment for mounting the M1917 Bayonet when procured for riot or guard duty.

Attempts to develop a satisfactory universal bayonet attachment for mounting an M1917 Bayonet on all of the selected shotguns were unsuccessful due to difference in construction of various makes of shotguns and the variations in dimensions, particularly in the outside diameter of the barrel, between individual guns of the same model and make. Consequently, a bayonet attachment for the Winchester M1897 and M12 Riot Type gun known as Attachment, Bayonet, Type W, and bayonet attachment for the Stevens M520-30 and M620A known as Attachment, Bayonet, Type S, were adopted as standard components in June 1944. At the same time the following action was taken;

a. The following shotguns, 12-gauge. Riot Type, were classified as commercial standard:

1. Winchester, M12 with cylinder bore barrel
2. Stevens, M520-30 with cylinder bore barrel
3. Stevens, M620A with cylinder bore barrel

b. The following shotguns, 12-gauge, Sporting Type, with 26-inch improved cylinder bore or 30-inch full choke barrel were classified as commercial standard articles:

1. Remington, M11A and "Sportsman" Sporting Type
2. Remington, M31
3. Winchester, M12

c. The following shotguns, 12-gauge, were classified as commercial limited standard:

1. Winchester, M1897 Riot and Sporting Type
2. Savage, M720C
3. Ithaca, M37

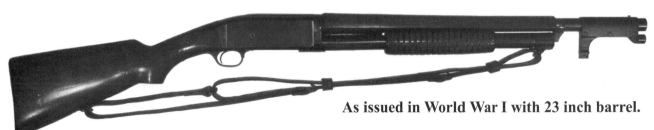

As issued in World War I with 23 inch barrel.

**Model 10 Remington Riot Type Shotgun with Wooden Hand Guard.
Though 3,500 Model 10 "Trench Guns" were bought in World War I, they were dropped in 1941
as "Standard" issue due to lack of spare parts. Remington had ceased its manufacture in 1928.**

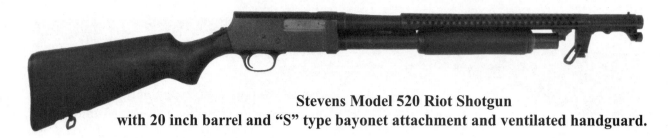

Stevens Model 520 Riot Shotgun
with 20 inch barrel and "S" type bayonet attachment and ventilated handguard.

RIOT TYPE SHOTGUNS

20 INCH BARRELS

Remington Model 10

Remington, M31

Remington, M11

Savage, M720

Stevens, M520

Winchester, M12

To obtain exact comparative information on the performance, functioning, life, etc., of the various types of 12-gage shotguns being procured, the Aberdeen Proving Ground was directed in May 1944 to fire an endurance test to determine the following:

    a. Life in rounds-before major overhaul

    b. Rate of change of headspace

    c. Replacement parts required (by model and round)

    d. Malfunctions and stoppages (listed by cause and round)

The shotguns to be tested were the Winchester, M12, Remington, M11A, Remington "Sportsman", Remington, M31, Stevens, M620, Savage, M720C; Ithaca, M37, and the M97, Stevens, M520, 26-inch and 28-inch barrels, and Stevens, M620, 26-inch and 28-inch barrels.

Tests conducted at Aberdeen involved the firing of the various shotguns from the shoulder, and tests conducted at Air Force installations under supervision of Aberdeen personnel involved the firing from mounts.

Complete formal reports of these tests are, at this time, not available, however, informal reports indicate the following:

    a. For normal shooting the Remington, M31, and the Winchester, M12 are superior.

    b. For shooting from a mount a special shotgun should be developed to withstand the severe shock.

Stevens Model 620 Riot Shotgun
with 20 inch barrel and "S" type bayonet attachment and ventilated handguard.

Marine Corps Historical Center

"Marines hit Blue Beach #2 on Okinawa", 1st Marine Division, 1 April 1945. Photo by Pvt. Bob Bailey. The center Marine carries a 12 Gauge Model 12 Winchester "Trench" Shotgun.

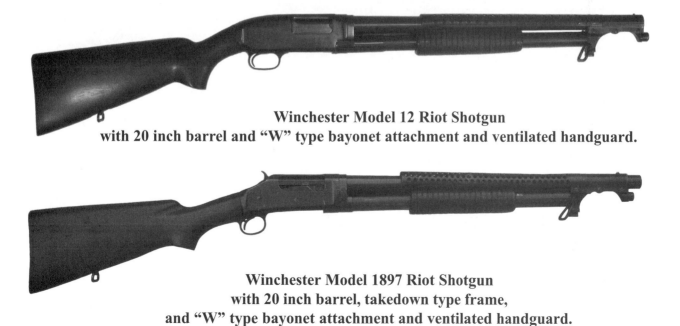

Winchester Model 12 Riot Shotgun
with 20 inch barrel and "W" type bayonet attachment and ventilated handguard.

Winchester Model 1897 Riot Shotgun
with 20 inch barrel, takedown type frame,
and "W" type bayonet attachment and ventilated handguard.

Harrington & Richardson Line Throwing Kit.

The 45-70 chambered Line Throwing gun is based on the H&R No. 6 single shot shotgun. It was offered to the military services by Harrington & Richardson in their 1942 H&R Reising Submachine Gun Manual, which doubled as their wartime small arms catalog.

"Gunnery students practice skeet shooting with their instructor, at NAS Jacksonville, Florida, 6 June 1942. This sport taught the students how to lead moving targets. Guns are Browning semi-automatic shotguns."

"USS Kearney, DD432. Crew members prepare to warp alongside tender, at Reykjavik, Iceland on 19 October 1941." The line throwing gun is a 45-70 chambered Harrington & Richardson shotgun.

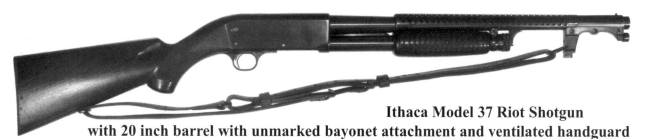

Ithaca Model 37 Riot Shotgun
with 20 inch barrel with unmarked bayonet attachment and ventilated handguard

GUN		Remington M10	Remington M31	Remington M11 and Sportsman	Winchester M97	Winchester M12	Ithaca M37	Stevens M520	Stevens M620	Stevens M720
Weight	Riot	7.5 lb.	6.9 lb	7.8 lb.	7.3 lb.	6.5 lb.	6.0 lb.	7.0 lb.	7.0 lb.	7.6 lb.
	Skeet	+	7.6 lb.	8.3 lb.	7.6 lb.	7.0 lb.	6.3 lb.	7.6 lb.	7.6 lb.	8.0 lb.
	Trap	7.8 lb.	7.8 lb.	8.5 lb.	7.8 lb.	7.4 lb.	6.6 lb.	7.8 lb.	7.8 lb.	8.3 lb.
Length overall	Riot	39.5 in.	40 in.	40 in.	39 in.	40 in.	40 in.	40 in	40 in	39.5 in.
	Skeet	+	46 in.	46 in.	45 in.	46 in.	46 in.	46 in.	46 in.	45.5 in.
	Trap	49.5 in.	50 in.	50 in.	49 in.	50 in.	50 in.	50 in.	50 in.	49.5 in.
Length barrel	Riot	20 in.	20 in.	20 in.	20 in.	20 in.	20 in.	20 in.	20 in.	20 in.
	Skeet	+	26 in.	26 in.	26 in.	26 in.	26 in.	26 in.	26 in.	26 in.
	Trap	30 in.	30 in.	30 in.	30 in.	30 in.	30 in.	30 in.	30 in.	30 in.
Gauge		12	12	12	12	12	12	12	12	12
Magazine capacity		5	3-4*	4-2^	5	5	4	5	5	4

+ Remington, Model 10 is not supplied as a skeet gun
* Remington Model 31 is furnished with magazine capacities of both 3 and 4 rounds
^ The manufacturer's designation of "Sportsman" is given to those models of the Remington M11 with 2 round magazine.

SPORTING TYPE SHOTGUNS

SKEET SHOTGUNS

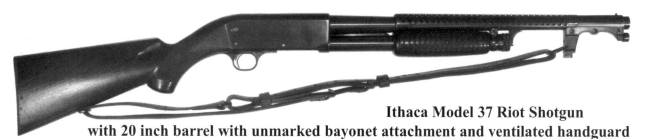

Remington, M31 - 26" Barrel

Remington Sportsman - 26" Barrel

Stevens, M620 - 26" Barrel

Winchester 1897 - 26" Barrel

TRAP SHOTGUNS

Ithaca, M37 - 30" Barrel

27 3/4" length: breech face to
muzzle of Cutts Compensator

Remington Sportsman with Cutts Compensator

Stevens, M620a - 30" Barrel

Winchester, M12 - 30" Barrel

Government Publications

Office of the Chief of Ordnance, Research & Development Service, *Record of Army Ordnance, Research and Development, Volume 2, Small Arms and Small Arms Ammunition,* Washington, DC, January 1946

Office of the Chief of Ordnance Technical Division, *Catalogue of Standard Ordnance Items*, 2nd Edition, Washington, DC, 1944

The 5th Division in France, Metz, France, December 1944

War Department, *America's Munitions, 1917-1918*, Report of Benedict Crowell, The Assistant Secretary of War, Director of Munitions, Government Printing Office, Washington, 1919

War Department, *FM23-5, War Department, Basic Field Manual, U.S. Rifle, Caliber .30, M1*, Raritan Arsenal, Washington, 30 July 1943

War Department, *FM23-7, War Department Basic Field Manual, U.S. Carbine, Caliber .30, M1 and M1A1*, Raritan Arsenal, 11 April 1944

War Department, *FM23-35, Basic Field Manual, Automatic Pistol, Caliber .45, M1911 and M1911A1*, Government Printing Office, Washington, April 30, 1940

War Department, *TM9-215, Technical Manual, Thompson Submachine Gun, Cal. .45, M1,* Raritan Arsenal, October 10, 1942

War Department, *TM9-280, Technical Manual, Caliber .22 Rifles, All Types,* Raritan Arsenal, 16 March 1944

War Department, *TM9-285, Technical Manual, Shotguns, All Types,* Raritan Arsenal, September 21, 1942

War Department, *TM9-1211, Technical Manual, Ordnance Maintenance, Cal. .30, Browning Automatic Rifle, M1918A2, Raritan Arsenal, September 1944*

War Department, *TM9-1270, Technical Manual, Ordnance Maintenance, U.S. Rifles, Cal. .30, M1903, M1903A1, M1903A3 and M1903A4, Raritan Arsenal,* 20 January1944

War Department, *TM9-1275, Technical Manual, Ordnance Maintenance, U.S. Rifles, Cal. .30, M1, M1C (Sniper's), and M1D (Sniper's)*, Government Printing Office, Washington, 1947

War Department, *TM9-1295, Technical Manual, Ordnance Maintenance, Pistols and Revolvers*, Raritan Arsenal, November 9, 1942

Published Works

Bady, Donald B., *Colt Automatic Pistols*, Borden Publishing Company, Alhambra, California, 1973

Battison, Edwin A., *Muskets to Mass Production, The Men & The Times that shaped American Manufacturing*, The American Precision Museum, Windsor, VT, 1976

Brophy, Lt. Col. William S., *Arsenal of Freedom, The Springfield Armory, 1890-1948*, Andrew Mowbray Publishers, Inc., Lincoln, Rhode Island, 1991

Brophy, Lt. Col. William S., *The Springfield 1903 Rifles*, Stackpole Books, Harrisburg, PA, 1985

Bruce, Robert, *"The M1 Does My Talking!"*, Sandstone, Virginia, 1992

Campbell, Clark S., *The '03 Springfield*, Ray Riling Arms Books Co., Philadelphia, Pennsylvania, 1981

Canfield, Bruce N., *A Collector's Guide to the M1 Garand and the M1 Carbine*, Andrew Mowbray Publishers, Inc., Lincoln, Rhode Island, 1988

Canfield, Bruce N., *A Collector's Guide to United States Combat Shotguns*, Andrew Mowbray Publishers, Inc., Lincoln, Rhode Island, 1992

Canfield, Bruce N., *A Collector's Guide to Winchester in the Service*, Andrew Mowbray Publishers, Inc., Lincoln, Rhode Island, 1991

Canfield, Bruce N., *U.S. Infantry Weapons of World War II*, Andrew Mowbray Publishers, Inc., Lincoln, Rhode Island, 1994 and 1996

Colvin, Fred H. and Ethan Viall, *United States Rifles and Machine Guns*, 1917, Reprinted as *Manufacture of the Model 1903 Springfield Service Rifle*, Wolfe Publishing Co. Inc., Prescott, Arizona, 1984

Duff, Scott A., *The M1 Garand: World War II,* Export, Pennsylvania, 1993

Ferris, C.S., *Rock Island Rifle, Model 1903*, Scott A. Duff Publications, Export, Pennsylvania, 2001

Flayderman, Norm, *Flayderman's Guide to Antique American Firearms*, 2nd Edition, Northfield, Illinois, 1980

Grant, Ellsworth S., *The Colt Armory*, Andrew Mowbray Publishers, Inc., Lincoln, Rhode Island, 1994

Hardin, Albert Nolan, Jr., *The American Bayonet, 1776 – 1964*, Published by Albert N. Hardin, Jr., Pennsauken, New Jersey, First Printing 1964, Second Printing by Meridian Gravure Company, Meridian, CT, 1977

Harrington & Richardson Arms Co., *Manual, H&R Reising Submachine Gun*, Worcester, Massachusetts, 1942

Hatcher, Maj. Gen. Julian S. Hatcher, *The Book of the Garand*, 1948, Reprint, The Gun Room Press, 1977

Hatcher, Maj. Gen. Julian S. Hatcher, *Hatcher's Notebook*, 1947, Reprint, Stackpole Books, Harrisburg, PA, 1962

Hicks, Major James E., *U.S. Firearms 1776-1956, Notes on U.S. Ordnance Vol. 1*, Illustrated by Andre Janot, La Canada, California, 1957

Iannamico, Frank, *The Reising Submachine Gun Story*, Moose Lake Publishing, Harmony Maine, 1999

Jinks, Roy G., *History of Smith & Wesson*, 1977, Revised, Beinfeld Publishing, 1988

Pate, Charles W., *U.S. Handguns of World War II, The Secondary Pistols and Revolvers*, Andrew Mowbray Publishers, Inc., Lincoln, Rhode Island, 1994

Rankin, Colonel Robert H., USMC, *Small Arms of the Sea Services*, N. Flayderman & Co., Inc., New Milford, Connecticut, 1972

Ruth, Larry, *The M1 Carbine, Design, Development, Production*, Desert Publications, Cornville, Arizona, 1979

Sharpe, Philip B., *The Rifle in America*, 1938, Revised, Funk & Wagnalls Company, New York, 1947

Skennerton, Ian, *The U.S. Enfield,* Margate, Australia, 1983

Manuscript - *John E. & Frank W. Green & the Crusade thru Europe*, Joseph T. Green, 1998